D0991384

THE CHEMISTRY OF NATURAL PRODUCTS

K. W. BENTLEY, *Editor*

Volume I

THE ALKALOIDS

By K. W. Bentley

Volume II

MONO- AND SESQUITERPENOIDS

By P. de Mayo

Volume III

THE HIGHER TERPENOIDS

By P. de Mayo

Additional volumes in preparation

THE CHEMISTRY OF NATURAL PRODUCTS
A series of texts on the constitution of natural products

K. W. BENTLEY, *Editor*

VOLUME III

THE
HIGHER TERPENOIDS

P. de Mayo

Imperial College of Science and Technology
London, England

19 59

INTERSCIENCE PUBLISHERS, INC., NEW YORK
INTERSCIENCE PUBLISHERS LTD., LONDON

Library of Congress Catalog Card Number 58-59772

Copyright © 1959 by

INTERSCIENCE PUBLISHERS, INC.

QD
416
.D45H
1959
cop. 1

INTERSCIENCE PUBLISHERS, INC.
250 Fifth Avenue, New York 1, N.Y.

For Great Britain and Northern Ireland:
INTERSCIENCE PUBLISHERS LTD.
88/90 Chancery Lane, London, W.C. 2, England

PRINTED IN THE UNITED STATES OF AMERICA

PREFACE

"Hallo, Rabbit," Pooh said, "is that you?"
"Let's pretend it isn't," said Rabbit, "and see what happens."
—A. A. MILNE

The terpenoids are amongst the oldest studied of natural products, and have, therefore, long held a place in degree courses. When subjected to the study of these compounds the student, the author feels, has a tendency to divide terpenoids into two classes: the dull, but venerable, monoterpenoids and the *parvenu* triterpenoids, the latter being really too complex and bizarre to be of interest to any but the specialist. The rest is silence, with the exception, perhaps, of an occasional murmur about the unfairness of Hrn. Wagner and Meerwein. This is a pity because the terpenoids are also very exciting.

Probably the most distinctive feature of terpenoid compounds is the prodigious facility with which they undergo cyclisation and re-arrangement, and it is just this which has added the difficulty and interest to their study. Some of the structural contortions undergone by, say, the triterpenoids, are such that a very few years ago they would have been considered incredible. Even with the simpler monoterpenoids the older workers found that during their study the substance investigated had promptly changed into something else, and only by assuming that it *had* changed could progress be made. The manner by which the change was brought about was not studied until much later, and indeed is still being so. The spinal rearrangement of friedelin, the many cyclisations of caryophyllene, and the acid-, base-, and light-induced transformations of santonin are gymnastic processes of an interest comparable to any in organic chemistry.

But stimulation is not all that may be garnered from a study of the terpenoids. Aside from a clearer concept of the versatility of carbonium ion rearrangements, it will be found that these substances represent a useful framework upon which very many general chemical reactions may be studied. These include, apart from synthetic and degradative processes, examples of the stereochemical requirements of reactions and of the relationship of stereochemistry and stability and other physical properties. In a sense, correctly studied, terpenoids present almost a microcosm of organic chemistry. In the present work the mono- and sesquiterpenoids have been covered, the higher terpenoids being reserved for the next volume in this series.

No study of the terpenoids could be written which was not greatly indebted to the many volumes of Simonsen's *The Terpenes*, Guenther's *The Essential Oils*, and Gildemeister's *Die aetherischen Öle.* In addition, the author would like to thank Dr. W. C. J. Ross for a view of volumes IV and V of *The Terpenes* prior to publication. He is indebted to his many colleagues, including, Drs. A. S. Kende, S. K. Pradhan, A. I. Scott, M. Shafiq, and J. K. Sutherland for helpful and often pointed criticism, and especially to Drs. G. Morrison and C. J. W. Brooks for reading the entire manuscript.

A particular debt of gratitude is due to Professor D. H. R. Barton, F.R.S., for an inexhaustible supply of keen and constructive criticism in the reading of the whole manuscript, and for devoting much time and enthusiasm to the discussion of its many problems.

Glasgow, Scotland   PAUL DE MAYO
April, 1957

CONTENTS

CHAPTER 1

THE DITERPENOIDS

Many of the diterpenoids, particularly the resin acids, have been known for over a century, but comparatively little progress in their chemistry was made until about 1930. Since then there have been rapid advances, and at present the structures of most of the major known diterpenoids have been elucidated.

Probably of greatest historical interest have been the researches carried out on the resin acids, but two of the most interesting individual substances, marrubiin and columbin, are bitter principles.

THE RESIN ACIDS

Incisions cut in the bark of pine trees result in the formation and exudation of an oleoresin. This can be separated by stream distillation into a volatile fraction (turpentine) and a residue, which, when cold, sets to a brown glass. The latter is known as rosin or colophony. Turpentine consists mainly of the bicyclic monoterpenoid pinene. Rosin, on the other hand, is a complex mixture of acids largely of the formula $C_{19}H_{29} \cdot COOH$. A major constituent of rosin is abietic acid, which is comparatively stable though very sensitive to air oxidation even when pure. Abietic acid is, however, only a minor constituent of the un-steam-distilled oleoresin, and is formed from a number of labile precursors. The isolation of these so-called primary acids has been a problem of some difficulty since extensive changes take place during the collection and in the storage of the undistilled oleoresin. However, storage of the freshly collected oleoresin at low temperature results in the separation, as a crystalline cake, of some acidic components. This crude mixture is known as galipot. In the literature a very large number of acids are reported derived from galipots from different sources. Many of these are, however, mixtures of comparatively few acids. The difficulties are engendered by the formation of mixed crystals and the lack of reliable criteria of purity. Melting points in this series have a wide range even with pure substances.

Abietic acid (I) is by far the most important of the resin acids and can be prepared from rosin by the action of heat or of acids. The serious investigations of its structure may be said to have begun in 1903, when Vesterberg (1) dehydrogenated abietic acid with sulphur and obtained retene (II).

The determination of the structure of retene was difficult, and was rendered even more so by the faulty analyses obtained with the macro method of combustion used. By modification of the combustion technique Bamberger and Hooker (2) were able to correlate previous work with their own, and they proved that retene was a methyl*iso*propylphenanthrene. They also showed that one alkyl group was at C_1, whilst the other was *not* at C_2, C_9, or C_{10}. Little further progress was made until 1910, when Bucher (3) completed

(1)

(11)

the elucidation of the structure. Some of the more essential experiments of these workers are summarised opposite.

Retenequinone (III), obtained by oxidation of retene, gives with
alkaline permanganate the key intermediate (IV). Further oxidation
of this to (IX) and cleavage with very vigorous alkaline treatment
gives the acid (X). Since (IX) does not form an anhydride and (X)
does, one of the carboxyl (and therefore one of the alkyl) groups
must be *ortho* to the centre ring and hence at C_1 in phenanthrene.
The skeleton of (IX) and (X) follow from their conversion to fluorenone (XII) and diphenyl (XI). The fact that (IV) is an acid with
the same number of carbon atoms as retene, less one lost in the
fluorenone formation, suggests that the carboxyl is derived from a
methyl group. The conversion of (IV) to (VII) through (V) and (VI)
(in which the exact position of one carboxyl is not known) shows
that it is the methyl group that is at C_1. This could not have been
derived from the other series of degradations since (X) is ambiguous
as regards the particular alkyl precursor of the carboxyl groups.
Oxidation of the *iso*propyldiphenyl to diphenyl-4-carboxylic acid, a
known substance, established the position of the *iso*propyl group
in retene.

The completion of the structural problem of retene accounted for
18 of the 20 carbon atoms in abietic acid. One of the two atoms
missing was eliminated as carbon dioxide and, since non-angular
alkyl groups in perhydroaromatic rings appeared to survive dehydrogenation, it was presumed that the remaining carbon atom was
attached to a quaternary centre. By vigorous oxidation of abietic
acid with potassium permanganate Ruzicka and his co-workers (4)

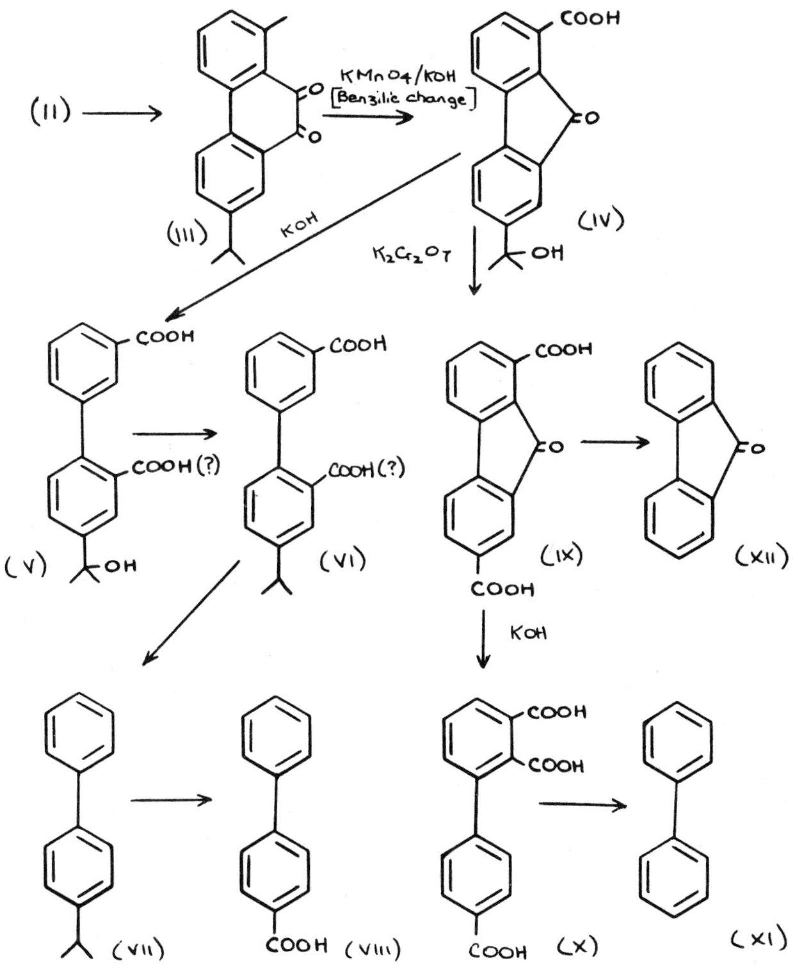
(II)
KMnO4/KOH
[Benzilic change]
(III)
(IV)
COOH
O
OH
KOH
K2Cr2O7
COOH
COOH (?)
(V)
(VI)
(IX)
(XII)
KOH
(VII)
(VIII)
(X)
(XI)

succeeded in isolating two acids, (XIII) and (XIV). These fragments represented ring A of abietic acid since the nuclear methyl
group was present and because the disruption of ring B could lead to
the presence of only two carboxyl groups in these acids, the third
represented the original carboxyl group of abietic acid. The relative position of the methyl groups was shown by dehydrogenation.
The problem remaining was the location of the carboxyl group and
of the double bonds. It was noted in the early stages that the carboxyl group of abietic acid was very hindered and might therefore
be tertiary. In 1922 Ruzicka and Meyer (5) carried out the series of
transformations shown opposite, since the product, methylretene,
had *not* lost a methyl group they concluded that the carboxyl group
was not at an angular position. It was not realised that with the
phosphorus pentachloride a rearrangement of the Wagner type had
taken place. Complexities soon arose, and the correct solution to
the problem was achieved independently by two groups. By oxidation of methylretene (homoretene) with alkaline ferricyanide, phe-
nanthrene-1 : 7-dicarboxylic acid was obtained, the same substance
as obtained by the oxidation of retene. The "extra" methyl group
was therefore not in the nucleus. This work by Ruzicka and his
collaborators (6) was complemented by that of Haworth (7) who in
1934 concluded that an ethyl group must be present and confirmed
this by synthesis of methylretene.

The two double bonds in abietic acid are conjugated ($\lambda_{max.}$ 241 mμ)
as shown originally by diazo coupling with p-nitrobenzenediazonium
chloride. Abietic acid does give a maleic anhydride adduct, suggestive of a *cis*oid arrangement of double bonds, at temperatures
above 100°, but the derivative obtained is the same as that from
levopimaric acid, an isomer. From levopimaric acid, however, the
adduct is formed at room temperature, and it is in the formation of the
adduct from abietic acid, then, that rearrangement takes place. The
position of one of the double bonds in abietic acid is clearly shown

"Methylretene"

by the transformation shown opposite, confirmed by the isolation of *iso*butyric acid on vigorous oxidation. The conversion of (XV) into (XVI) involves disproportionation of the intermediate dihydropyridine.

The stereochemistry of abietic acid has also been elucidated. The acid (XIV), now written (XVII), is optically inactive and so must possess a plane of symmetry. This is only possible if the 1 and 3 carboxyl groups are in the *cis* relationship to each other. A study of the dissociation constants of this acid by Barton and Schmeidler revealed that the centre carboxyl was *trans* to the other two. Hence the acid has the stereochemistry in (XVIII) and, provided no inversion takes place in the derivation of the acid—a fact confirmed in other ways—the fusion of rings A and B in abietic acid must be *trans*. Evidence against this was the fact that certain

(XV)

(XVI)

(XVII)

(XVIII)

dihydroabietic acids (e.g., (XIX)) on treatment with strong acids gave an isomeric lactone, the structure of which was believed to be (XX). However, such a formulation is impossible with a *trans*-fused A/B junction, and Barton (8) proposed that its formation involved methyl migration leading to the structure (XXI). Some years later this deduction was confirmed by Subluskey and Sanderson and by Velluz and his colleagues (9).

The remaining asymmetric centre in abietic acid is that at C_9. Since abietic acid is formed from other related acids by acid-cata-lysed transformations involving double bond migration, it was con-cluded (10) that the hydrogen atom at C_9 must be *trans* to the bridge-head methyl group, that is, in the more stable form. This is supported by molecular rotation (11) evidence which also leads to the abso-lute configuration (XXII). Final proof of the *trans* A/B junction and of the absolute configuration came with the derivation of the dicarboxylic acid (XXIII) from both abietic acid and from ergosterol-D (XXIV) (12). Other relationships between the diterpenoids and the steroids, and also between the di- and triterpenoids, have been established.

Dehydroabietic acid (XXV) was first obtained in a pure condition by Fieser and Campbell by the stages shown. It may be prepared by a number of other methods such as the action of N-bromosuc-cinimide on abietic acid methyl ester. An important step forward in diterpenoid chemistry was the total synthesis of dehydroabietic

(XIX)   (XXI)   (XX)

(XXIV)   (XXIII)   (XXII)

(XXV)

acid by Stork and Schulenberg (13). The steps are briefly outlined opposite. A stage of particular interest, the monomethylation of the tetralone, was achieved by methylation of the pyrrolidine enamine (14) with methyl iodide.

The nomenclature of the remaining resin acids is very confused. Levopimaric acid is not, for instance, the enantiomer of dextropi-

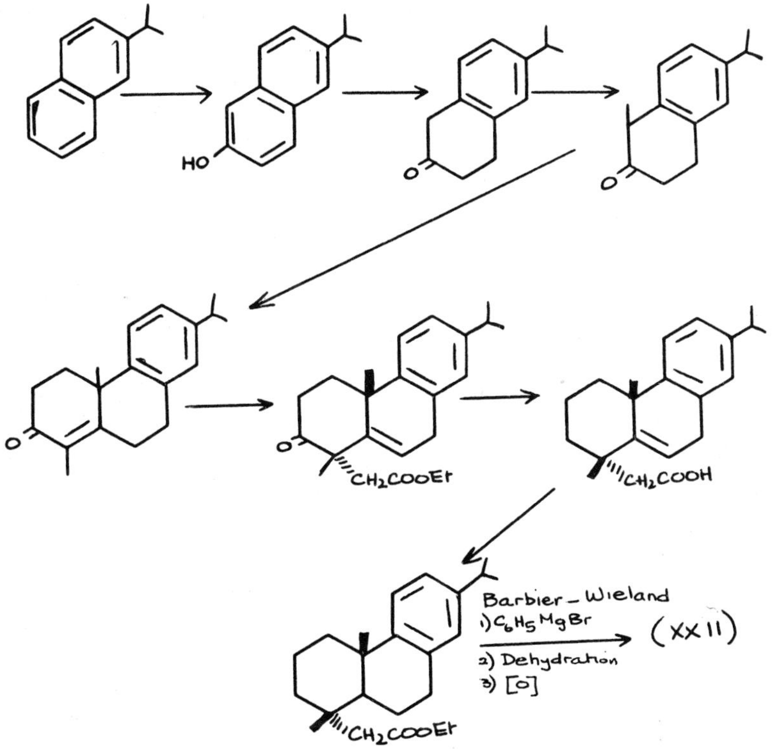

Barbier – Wieland
1) C_6H_5MgBr
2) Dehydration
3) [O]

(XXII)

CH_2COOEt

maric acid (also written D-pimaric acid). Levopimaric acid (XXVI) has been obtained from the galipots of French pine (*Pinus maritima*) and of *Pinus palustris*. It is a homoannular diene as shown by its ultra-violet absorption (λ_{max}. 272.5 mμ). As already mentioned (page 6), it readily gives a maleic anhydride adduct (XXVII). An interesting abnormal reaction takes place on ozonolysis of the adduct: two products formed by allylic oxidation, (XXVIII) and (XXIX), are obtained. The reason for the abnormal course may lie in the considerable steric hindrance of the double bond. Levopimaric acid differs from abietic acid only in the disposition of the double bonds and is thermally unstable with regard to it.

Another related compound is **neoabietic** acid (XXX). At 300° this is in thermal equilibrium with abietic acid and can be isolated from the mixture by fractional crystallisation of various salts. With acid it is converted to abietic acid. Its structure was proven by ozonolysis in stages, followed by dehydrogenation with palladised charcoal. The retention of the carboxyl carbon during the dehydrogenation is surprising (15).

The resin acids so far mentioned have a common carbon skeleton. Compounds having a somewhat different structure are also known.

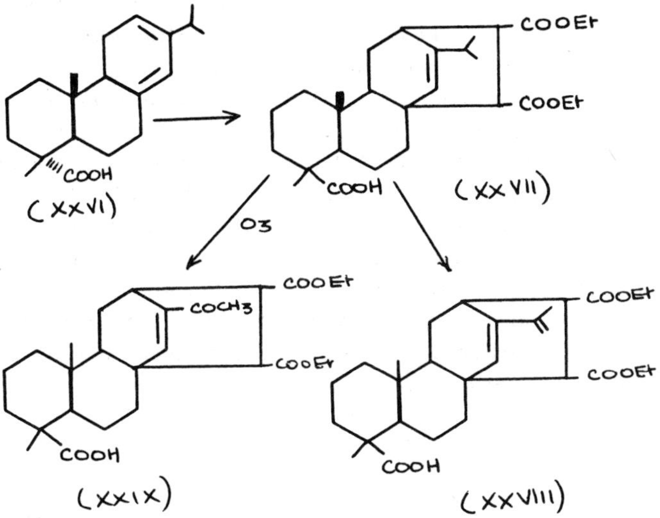

(XXVI)

(XXVII)

O_3

(XXIX)

(XXVIII)

(XXX)

+ CH_3COCH_3

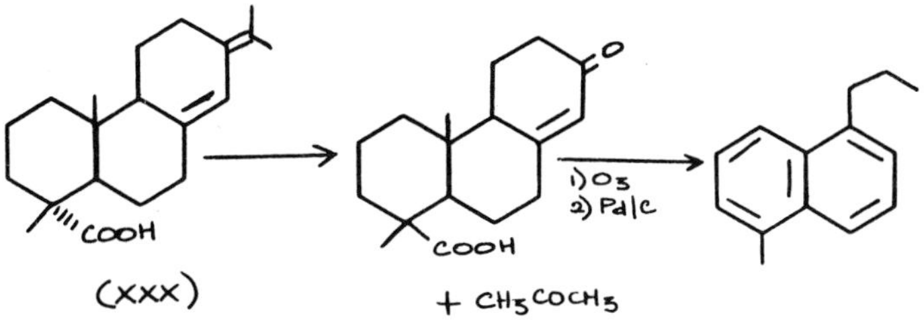

i) O_3
2) Pd/c

Dextropimaric acid (XXXI) has been isolated from French galipot; it is stable both to heat and acid. Isodextropimaric acid (XXXII) had usually been stated to be epimeric at C_{13}, and evidence to support this has been advanced. Thus ozonolysis of both acids, for instance, gave the same tricarboxylic acid. It has, however, recently been suggested (16) that the two acids differ at C_9 and that isodextropimaric acid is represented by (XXXIV). The formation of the common derivative (XXXIII) then involves equilibration α to the carbonyl group. This view is probably correct and is supported by the production of the *same* hydrocarbon, though admittedly with no optical activity, by the partial dehydrogenation of both dextro- and isodextropimaric acids. The problem appears to require further investigation.

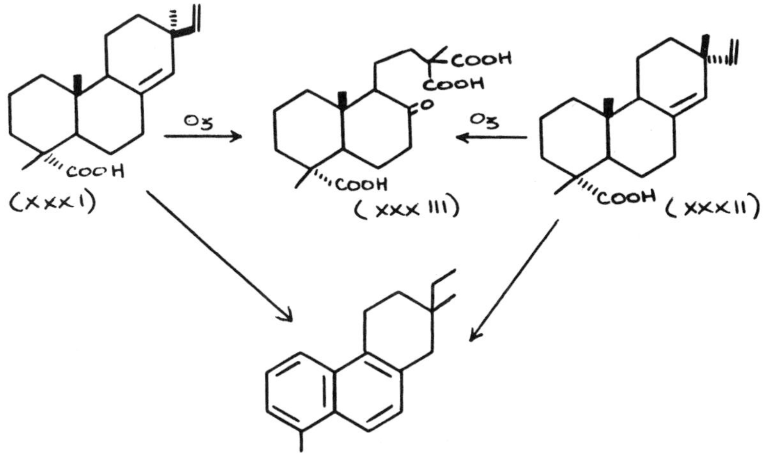
COOH
(XXXI)
O_3
COOH
COOH
COOH
(XXXIII)
O_3
COOH
(XXXII)

Agathenedicarboxylic acid (also known as agathic acid) (XXXV)
is a bicyclic resin acid first isolated from kauri and Manila copal
(44). It contains an *exo* methylene group, and the remaining double
bond is conjugated with a carboxyl group. On pyrolysis, passing
presumably through the $\beta:\gamma$-unsaturated isomer, the acid is decarboxylated to give noragathenedicarboxylic acid (XXXVI). Some
of the structural evidence is summarised opposite. By boiling with
formic acid agathenedicarboxylic acid is isomerised to a tricyclic
$\alpha:\beta$-unsaturated acid, *iso*agathenedicarboxylic acid (XXXVII). A
point of stereochemical difference between (XXXV) and the previously mentioned resin acids is that the configuration of the nuclear carboxyl group is inverted. In (XXXV) it is axial, and this
is reflected in the greater difficulty of hydrolysis of the esters of
agathenedicarboxylic acid; the acid may, therefore, be represented
the stereoformula (XXXVIII).

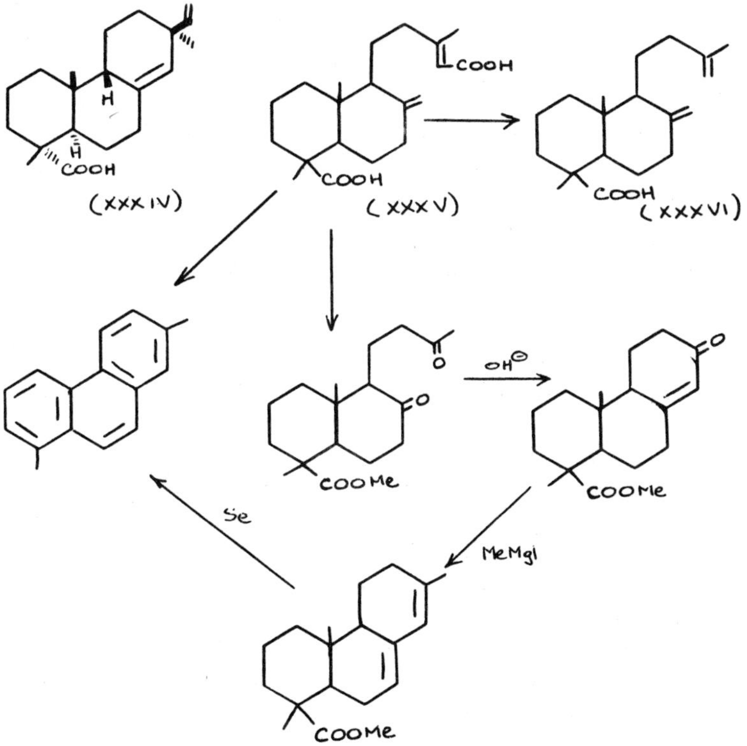

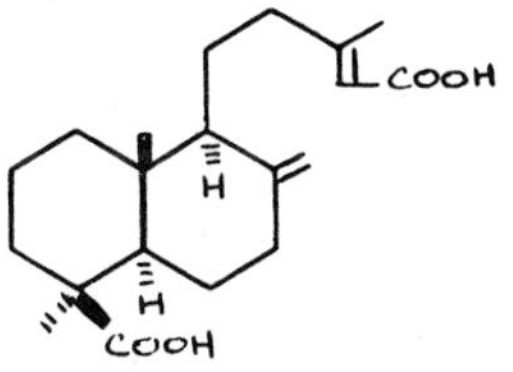

(XXXIV)

(XXXV)

(XXXVI)

OH⊖

Se

MeMgl

COOMe

COOMe

COOMe

(XXXVIII)

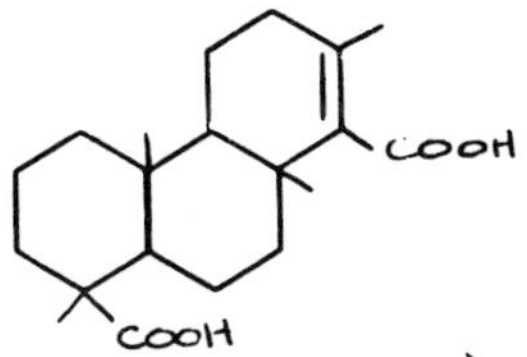

(XXXVII)

The basic skeleton of agathenedicarboxylic acid is the 13:14-seco-pimarane structure (XXXIX). This may be derived, theoretically, by fission of pimarane (XL), which is the hydrocarbon, apart from stereochemistry, on which the structures of dextro- and *iso*dextropimaric acids are based. A number of other acids have this *seco*-pimarane skeleton. Eperuic acid is the chief constituent of the oleoresin derived from *Eperua falcata*. Its structure was clearly elucidated by King and Jones (17) and was believed to be represented by (XLIa). Very recently, however, **labdanolic** acid, isolated from gum labdanum (22), has been conclusively shown to possess the structure and stereoehemistry indicated in (XLII). A comparison of the constants of corresponding degradation products shows that these are essentially identical except in that the *sign* of the rotations is always opposite. This has led to the proposal that the corresponding derivatives of the two acids are enantiomers. Since labdanolic acid has been directly related to substances of known absolute configuration it would seem that eperuic acid must be represented by (XLIb). It has, therefore, a carbon skeleton which is the mirror image of rings A and B of all the known di- and triterpenoids and of the steroids.

Cativic acid (XLIII) is a compound closely related (18) to (XLI) found in the oleoresin from *Priona copaifera*. **Sandaracopimaric acid**, from sandarac resin, has been stated to differ from either dextro- or *iso*dextropimaric acid in the configuration of the carboxyl group (19).

Podocarpic acid (XLIV) is not strictly a diterpenoid since it lacks the three carbon atom side-chain. It is usually included, however, because its chemistry is closely associated with these substances. It was first isolated in 1873 from the resin of *Podocarpus cupressinum*, but has since been found in a number of other resins. Its structure was proven by reduction of the acid methyl ether by the Rosenmund method (hydrogenation of the acid chloride with a poisoned catalyst) to the aldehyde. This was then reduced further to the alcohol which was dehydrated (with rearrangement) and then dehydrogenated to give 1-ethyl-6-methoxyphenanthrene (XLV). The configuration of the carboxyl group is the same as in agathenedicarboxylic acid and opposite to that of abietic acid. This con-

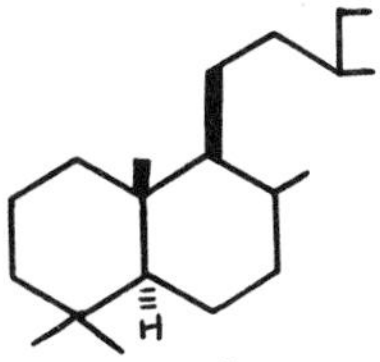

(XXXIX)

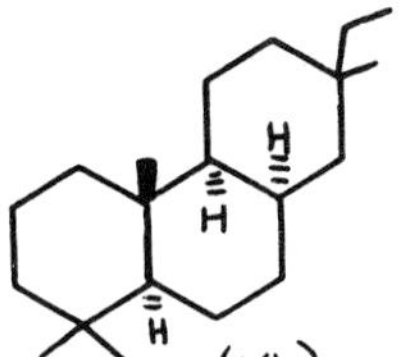

(XL)

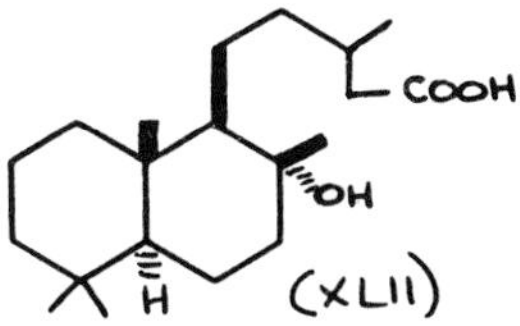

(XLII)

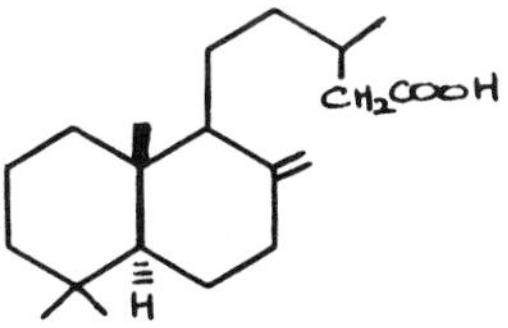

(XLIa)

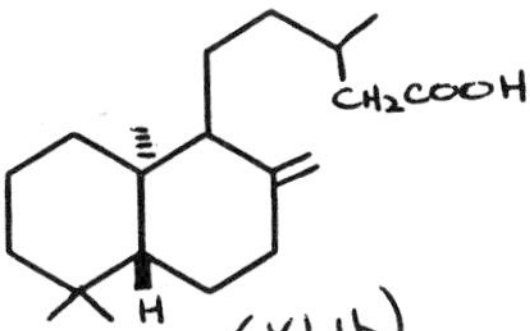

(XLIb)

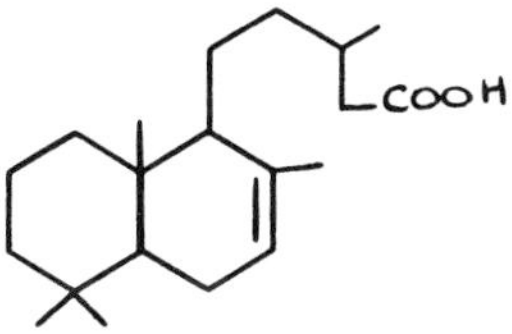

(XLIII)

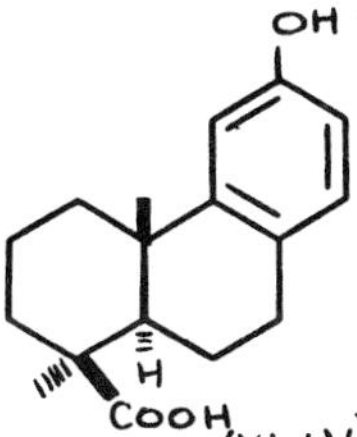

(XLIV)

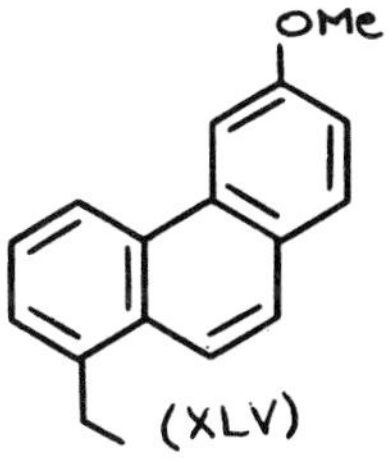

(XLV)

clusion was reached on the following evidence (20). Sulphonation of dehydroabietic acid gives the 12-sulphonate from which the corresponding phenol (XLVI) can be derived. This could be methylated by the action of methyl sulphate on the magnesio-chloride derivative to give, after esterification, (XLVII). The compound (XLVIII) obtained from podocarpic acid methyl ester methyl ether by the steps shown was not identical with (XLVII). By transforming both esters through the acid chlorides to the aldehydes and converting the carbonyl group to methylene by Wolff-Kishner reduction, the compound (XLIX) was obtained in both cases. The corresponding phenol is, in fact, a naturally occurring diterpenoid, ferruginol. The structure of podocarpic acid has been confirmed by the total synthesis of the racemate by King, King, and Topliss (23). The method was similar to that described below for ferruginol. Stereoisomers were separated by fractional crystallisation and chromatography.

The structure of **ferruginol** follows from its partial synthesis from dehydroabietic acid. A direct synthesis of ferruginol has been

(XLVI)   (XLVII)   (XLVIII)

(XLIX)

reported by King, King, and Topliss (21). (L) was prepared by the condensation of 2 : 2 : 6-trimethyl*cyclo*hexanone with sodio-methoxy-phenylacetylene. Ferruginol comprises the major part of the resin of the miro tree. From the Rimu tree Brandt and Thomas isolated 7-ketoferruginol (LI) and showed that it was identical with **sugiol,** a substance isolated from *Cryptomeria japonica.* Oxidation of ferruginol ethers or acetate with chromic acid results in the intro-duction of oxygen in the 7-position. Amongst related compounds may be mentioned **hinokiol,** isolated from the resin of the heartwood of *Chamaecyparis obtusa,* which is probably (LII), and **totarol** (LIII) (27a). It should be noted that totarol does not obey the isoprene rule; it has recently been synthesised (27b).

SUBSTANCES RELATED TO THE RESIN ACIDS

Vinhaticoic acid is a further example of a diterpenoid which does not obey the isoprene rule. This substance was isolated in 1953 from the heartwood of *Plathymenia reticula* Benth. as the methyl ester (24). It contained two ethylenic linkages as shown by quanti-tative hydrogenation and titration with monoperphthalic acid. This, together with the inert nature of the remaining third oxygen atom and the ultra-violet spectrum ($\lambda_{max.}$ 220 mμ) suggested the presence of a furan ring. This was confirmed by the formation of a maleic

(L)

P₂O₅

MeMgI

(LI)

(LII)

(LIII)

anhydride adduct. The ester (LIV) was then degraded stepwise to the ketone (LV). This ketone on Wolff-Kishner reduction and de-hydrogenation gave 1 : 8-dimethylphenanthrene (LVI). Reaction with methylmagnesium iodide and dehydrogenation gave (LVII). ˙In this compound the introduced methyl group at C_6 (phenanthrene numbering) marks the position of the ketone in (LV) and, therefore, of the furan oxygen in the original ester. Two positions are then possible for the furan ring—as in (LIV) and (LVIII). Dehydrogena-

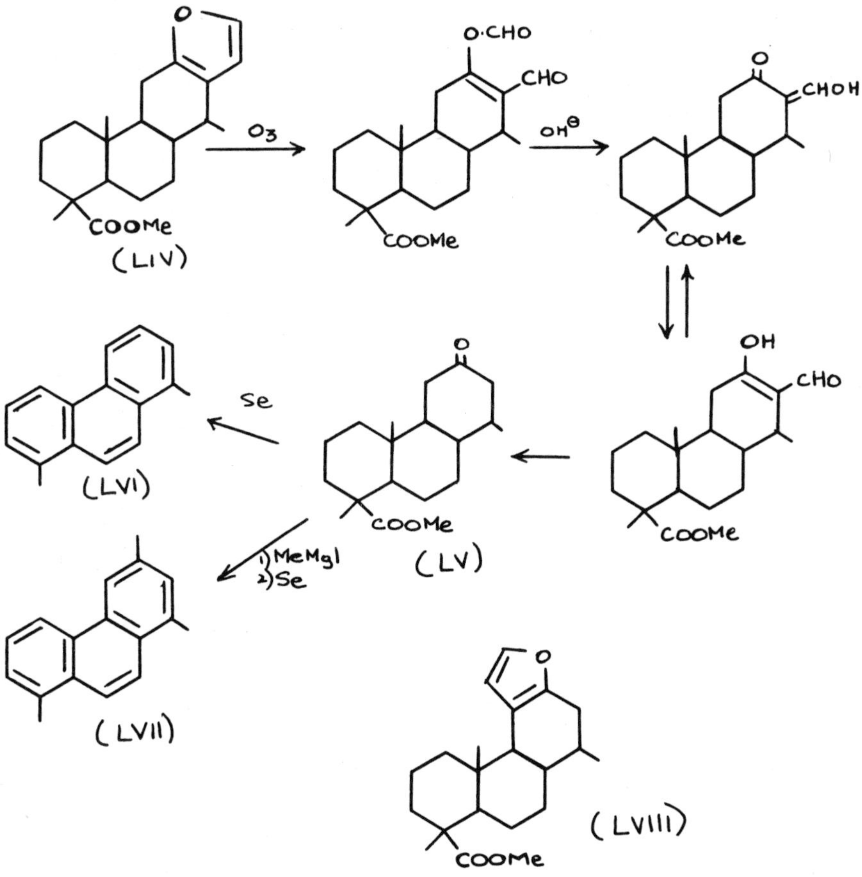
O·CHO
CHO
O
CHOH
COOMe
(LIV)
O_3
$OH^{\ominus}$
OH
CHO
O
Se
(LVI)
1) MeMgI
2) Se
(LV)
(LVII)
(LVIII)

tion of (LIV) with sulphur resulted in partial aromatisation to give
(LIX). This was then degraded to the phenolic aldehyde with ozone
and reduced by the Wolff-Kishner method to (LX). Selenium dehydrogenation then gave (LXI) and (LXII). The introduced methyl
group here marked the other furan terminus. These results establish
all but the position of the carboxyl group in vinhaticoic acid. This
was ascertained by reduction of the acid to the alcohol with lithium
aluminum hydride, dehydration with phosphorus pentachloride (with
rearrangement), and selenium dehydrogenation to give (LXIII). The
rate of hydrolysis of the ester suggested that the carboxyl was
equatorial (as in abietic acid) and this was confirmed by the fact
that the ester reacted with phenylmagnesium iodide to give the
diphenylcarbinol under conditions when methyl podocarpate does not
react. Vinhaticoic acid may therefore be presented by the stereoformula (LXIV). Since (LXIV) is a formula not in accord with the
isoprene rule, it was considered possible that vinhaticoic acid
might be (LXV), methyl migration taking place during dehydrogenation. Dehydrogenation of (LXVI) as a model compound gave, however, only pimanthrene (LXVII) with loss of the angular methyl
groups. The *trans* junction of the rings A and B in (LXIV) is by
analogy.

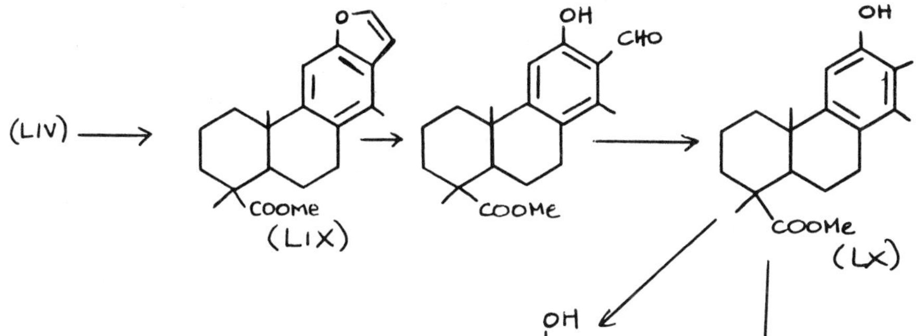

$(LIV) \longrightarrow$

(LIX)

(LX)

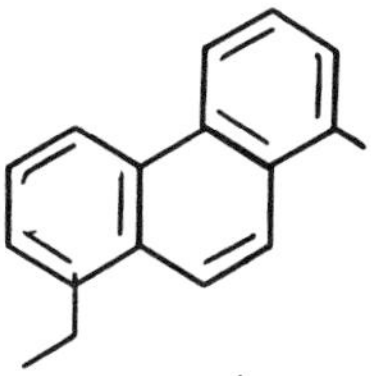

(LXIII)

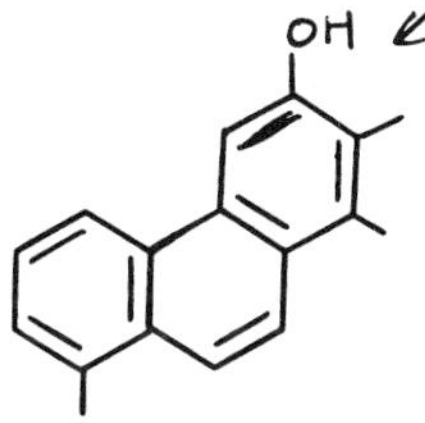

(LXI)

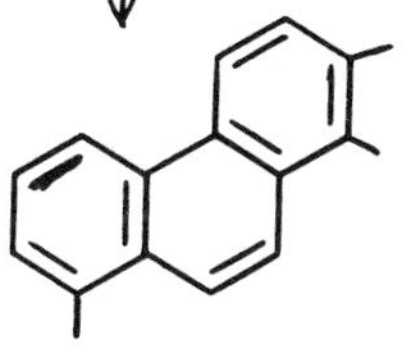

(LXII)

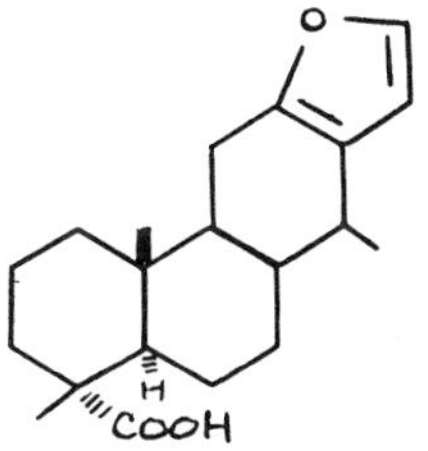

(LXIV)

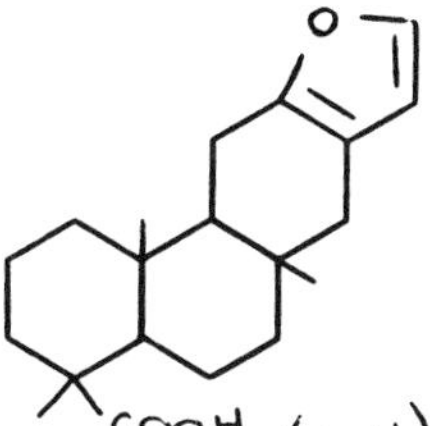

(LXV)

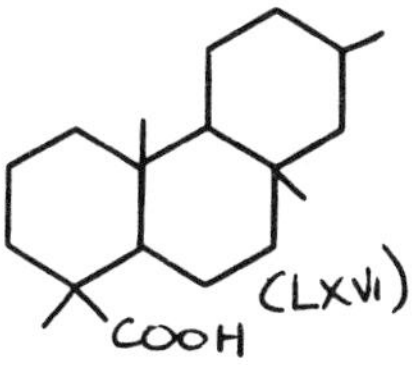

(LXVI)

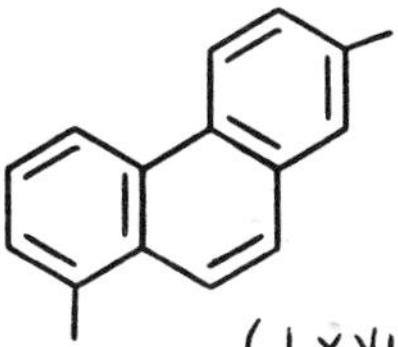

(LXVII)

From the heartwood of *Vouacapoua americana* Spoelstra, in 1930, isolated the methyl ester of an acid, **vouacapenic acid.** The substance was later obtained by King, Godson, and King (25) from *V. macropetala,* and their investigation revealed that the substance was closely allied to vinhaticoic acid. A number of degradations led to parallel results, and the relationship was rigorously established by conversion of both to the same partially deoxygenated substance (LXVIII). Vouacapenic acid (methyl ester) is therefore represented by (LXIX).

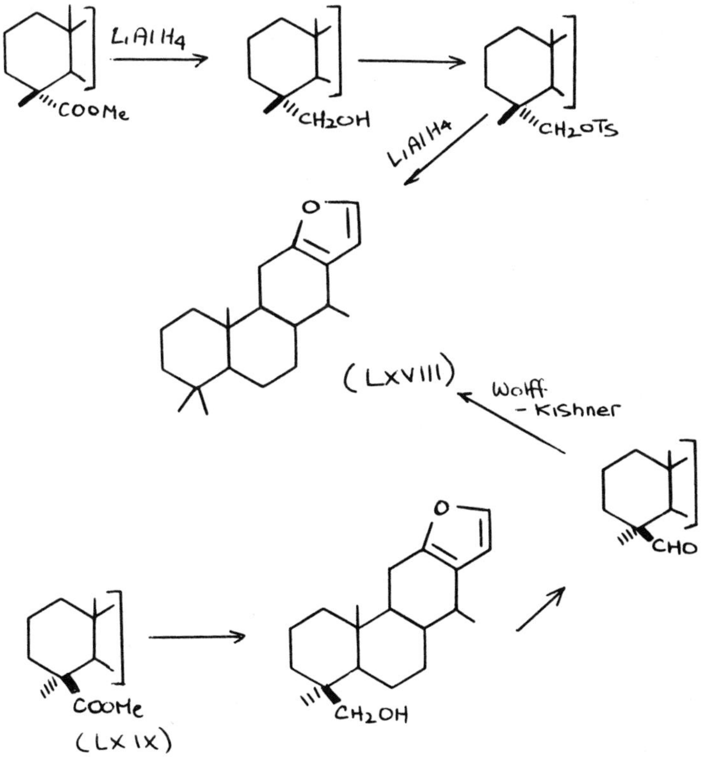
LiAlH4
COOMe
CH2OH
CH2OTs
LiAlH4
Wolff-Kishner
CHO
COOMe
CH2OH

(LXVIII)

(LXIX)

Sclareol (LXX) is a ditertiary glycol. It is a member of the 13 : 14-*seco*-pimarane group, and was first isolated in 1928 from the leaves of *Salvia sclarea*. A group of three closely related compounds, manool, manoyl oxide, and ketomanoyl oxide, also belong to this group. The alcohol **manool** (LXXI) was isolated from the wood oil of yellow pine; the other two compounds were isolated from the wood oil of the silver pine. The structure of manool was elucidated by Hosking and Brandt (26). Catalytic hydrogenation gave the saturated tetrahydromanool, proving the presence of two ethylenic linkages. Hydrogen chloride then gave (LXXII) which, after dehydrochlorination with aniline, on ozonolysis afforded (LXXIII) and (LXXIV). This provides evidence for the environment of the hydroxyl group. Ozonolysis of manool itself gave a C_{17} diketone in which the carbonyl groups were 1 : 5 to each other as shown by facile cyclisation to the hydroxy ketone (LXXV). The interesting conversion of (LXXI) into the 1 : 5-diketone on ozonol-

(LXX)

(LXXI)

(LXXII)

(LXXV)

(LXXIV)

(LXXIII)

(LXXVI)

ysis may proceed as shown opposite. The skeleton of manool was originally based on its relationship to sclareol, both alcohols giving the same trichloro compound (LXXVI) with hydrogen chloride—but direct evidence has been obtained by conversion, as shown, into a derivative of dehydroabietic acid, dehydroabietane (LXXVII). Manoyl oxide also gives (LXXVI) with hydrogen chloride and has the structure (LXXVIII). By the oxidation of manool with

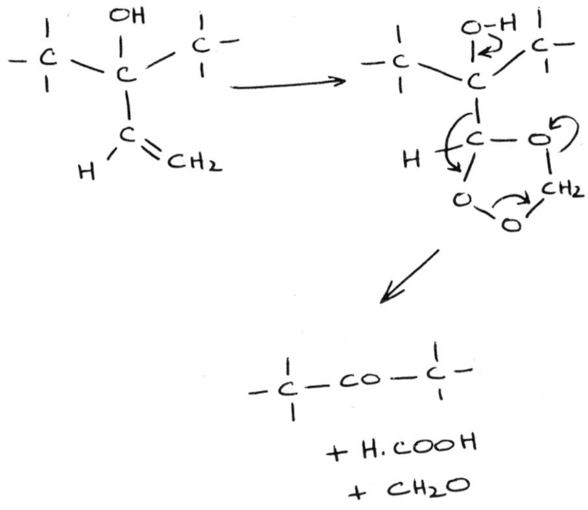

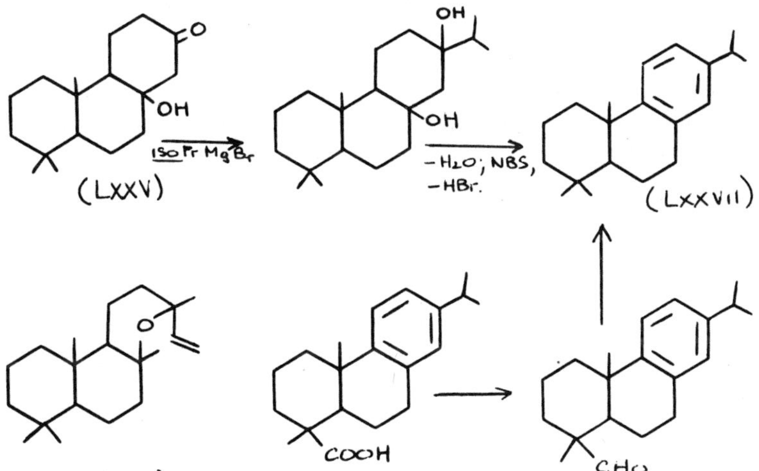

$$-\overset{|}{\underset{|}{C}}-\overset{OH}{\underset{|}{C}}-\overset{|}{\underset{|}{C}}- \longrightarrow -\overset{|}{\underset{|}{C}}-\overset{O-H}{\underset{|}{C}}/\overset{|}{\underset{|}{C}}-$$

$$-\overset{|}{\underset{|}{C}}-CO-\overset{|}{\underset{|}{C}}-$$

$$+ \ H.COOH$$

$$+ \ CH_2O$$

(LXXV)

isoPrMgBr

—H₂O; NBS,
—HBr.

(LXXVII)

(LXXVIII)

COOH

CHO

potassium permanganate the ketone (LXXIX) is obtained. This can be oxidised with hypobromite to the corresponding acid (LXXX) and with sulphuric acid-acetic acid is cyclised to ambreinolide (LXXXI), a product obtained by the degradation of ambrein (page 000). An interesting derivative of (LXXIX) is obtained with osmium tetroxide. It is the internal ketal (LXXXII). A similar product (LXXXIII) is obtained by osmic acid oxidation of dihydro-γ-ionone (LXXXIV).

The hydrocarbons **phyllocladene** (LXXXV) and **isophyllocladene** (LXXXVI) have been isolated from a large number of essential oils. Both hydrocarbons are tetracyclic and contain, in addition, one ethylenic linkage; they give the same hydrochloride. The structures (28) given are those proposed by Brandt.

Amongst other naturally occurring diterpenoid hydrocarbons may be mentioned (LXXXVII), isolated from oil of wormwood by Sorm and his co-workers (34). Another hydrocarbon, not strictly a diterpenoid, which is closely related to the resin acids is **fichtelite** (LXXXVIII) (38). This is found with retene in fossil resins and is completely saturated. It was first isolated by Fikentscher from pine trunk remains in a peat bed in Bavaria. It occurs to a large extent between the annual rings of the fossilised wood and undoubtedly is formed from resin acid precursors. As would be expected, it is chemically very resistant; on dehydrogenation it gives retene.

(LXXIX)   (LXXX)   (LXXXI)

OsO₄

(LXXXII)   (LXXXIII)   OsO₄   (LXXXIV)

(LXXXV)   (LXXXVI)

(LXXXVII)   (LXXXVIII)

Before passing on to a consideration of more complex diterpenoids mention must be made of the acyclic alcohol **phytol** (LXXXIX). This compound was found by Willstätter in 1907 in his classical researches to be the alcoholic moiety of chlorophyll. It is also the side-chain in the molecules of vitamin E (XC) and vitamin K_1 (XCI). Willstätter did not succeed in the complete elucidation of the phytol structure. This was resolved by Fischer (29), who, by ozonolysis, obtained a saturated ketone, $C_{18}H_{36}O$. This showed that the sole double bond in phytol was in the 2 : 3 position. By application of the isoprene rule Fischer concluded that the ketone might be 2 : 6 : 10-trimethyl-14-pentadecanone and proved his hypothesis by synthesis from hexahydrofarnesyl bromide. Later, he converted this to "phytol"; several other non-stereospecific syntheses have been since reported. It may be mentioned here that vitamin A (XCII), not usually considered with the terpenoids, falls into the diterpenoid class.

MORE COMPLEX DITERPENOIDS

Marrubiin is the bitter principle of horehound (*Marrubium vulgare*) and was first described by Harms in 1842. Preliminary investigations were made by a number of workers, but it was not until 1932 that it was first obtained in a pure state. The researches may be divided into two periods separated by the second war.

In the first period (30) it was established that marrubiin, $C_{20}H_{28}O_4$, was a lactone and hydrolysis readily gave marrubic acid, $C_{20}H_{30}O_5$. There were in addition two double bonds present because hydrogenation gave tetrahydromarrubiin. One of the remaining oxygen atoms was presumed a tertiary hydroxyl group since marrubiin could be dehydrated with phosphorus trichloride or thionyl chloride to give anhydromarrubiin. From the latter, by hydrolysis, anhydromarrubic acid and, by hydrogenation, hexahydroanhydromarrubiin were obtained. The remaining oxygen atom present was unreactive and so was presumed present in an oxide ring. This information led to the conclusion that marrubiin has a bicyclic carbon skeleton. Dehydrogenation with selenium gave 1 : 2 : 5-trimethylnaphthalene, and this suggested a relationship to manool and agathene dicarboxylic acid and the possibility of a *seco*-pimarane skeleton. These

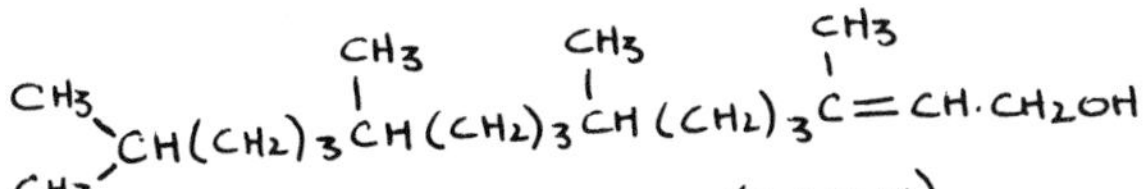

$$\underset{CH_3}{\overset{CH_3}{>}}CH(CH_2)_3\overset{\overset{\displaystyle CH_3}{|}}{CH}(CH_2)_3\overset{\overset{\displaystyle CH_3}{|}}{CH}(CH_2)_3\overset{\overset{\displaystyle CH_3}{|}}{C}=CH \cdot CH_2OH$$

(LXXXIX)

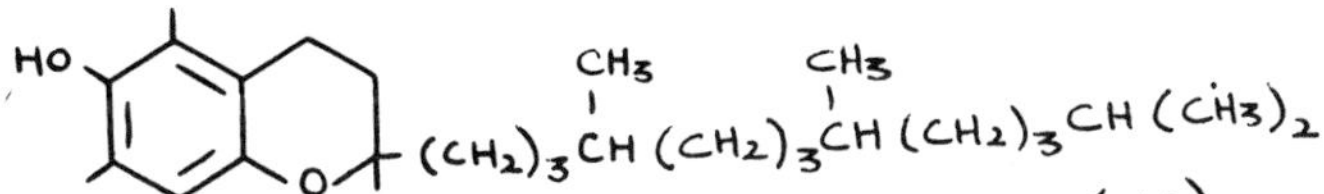

$(CH_2)_3\overset{\overset{\displaystyle CH_3}{|}}{CH}(CH_2)_3\overset{\overset{\displaystyle CH_3}{|}}{CH}(CH_2)_3CH(CH_3)_2$

(XC)

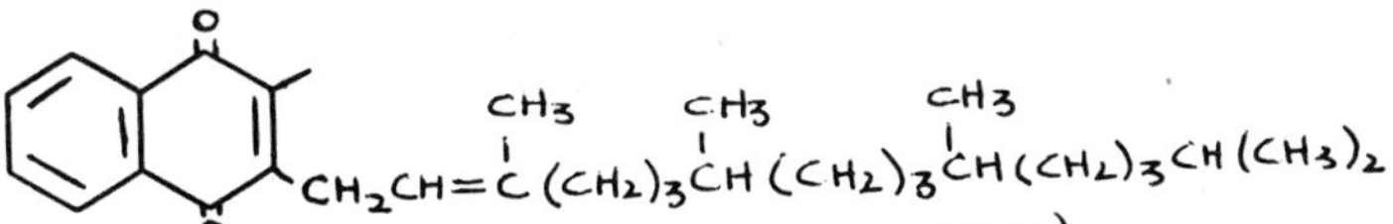

$CH_2CH=\overset{\overset{\displaystyle CH_3}{|}}{C}(CH_2)_3\overset{\overset{\displaystyle CH_3}{|}}{CH}(CH_2)_3\overset{\overset{\displaystyle CH_3}{|}}{CH}(CH_2)_3CH(CH_3)_2$

(XCI)

$CH=CH \cdot \overset{\overset{\displaystyle CH_3}{|}}{C}=CH \cdot CH=CH \cdot \overset{\overset{\displaystyle CH_3}{|}}{C}=CH \cdot CH_2OH$

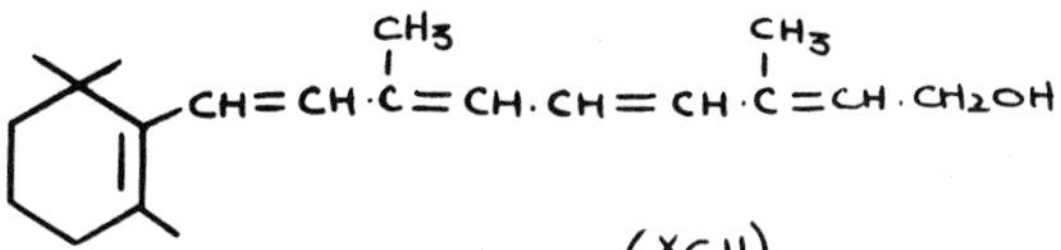

(XCII)

results may be summarised in the partial formula (XCIII). Marrubiin differed from manoyl oxide and related compounds in that it did not form tricyclic derivatives.

After some years, work was resumed on marrubiin by three schools of workers. Ghigi (31) found that on oxidation of marrubiin with chromic acid in acetic acid three carbon atoms were lost together with the inert oxygen. This was confirmed by Cocker and his co-workers (32) who corrected the formula of the product from $C_{17}H_{22}O_4$ to $C_{17}H_{24}O_4$. They concluded that since both double bonds were destroyed these results were best accommodated by a furan ring. They confirmed this conclusion by a study of the light absorption characteristics and colour reactions of marrubiin. This oxidation product was a dilactone, and from a study of infra-red spectra they concluded that the original lactone in marrubiin was a δ-lactone and the new one a γ-lactone, in part, because of its ready formation with the tertiary hydroxyl originally present. Hardy and Rigby (33) considered, however, that the relevant infra-red band (at 1765 cm^{-1}) was, in fact, that of a γ-lactone, and this view was later accepted also by the previous workers. The partial structure (XCIV) then followed from the available evidence. However, no rigid proof of the carbon skeleton had yet been adduced. Support for the placing of the tertiary hydroxyl group was obtained in the following way. Anhydrotetrahydromarrubiin on ozonolysis gave a keto-lactone $C_{14}H_{20}O_3$. In this reaction the entire side-chain is removed and the infra-red spectrum of the product shows the presence of the original γ-lactone and a band at 1706 cm^{-1} to be attributed to a carbonyl group, in a six-membered ring. Now the hydroxy acid obtained from this by hydrolysis does not lose carbon dioxide readily and so may be presumed not to be a β-keto acid. With the partial formula (XCIV) these results may be expressed as shown opposite.

If the carbon skeleton be correct then the carbon atoms marked with the asterisk cannot be the carboxyl since these are both β to the carbonyl group. Only the geminal positions remain. This leads

(XCIII)

(XCIV)

(XCIV) ⟶

to the structures (XCV) and (XCVI) for marrubiin. Evidence in favour of (XCV) was obtained by Cocker and his colleagues. Methyl marrubate on oxidation with chromic acid gave (XCVII), the loss of three carbon atoms and formation of a γ-lactone being accompanied in this case by oxidation of the hydroxyl of the original lactone to a ketone. The derived keto acid, with acetic anhydride, was cyclised to an enol lactone which could have been (XCVIII) or (XCIX). The product, reacted rapidly with bromine and with permanganate, was hydrolysed by mild acid treatment and on hydrogenation was reduced to a saturated acid in keeping with an enol-lactone formulation. Since the structure (C), derived from (XCVI) would have been an infringement of Bredt's rule this alternative structure for marrubiin was rejected.

The same conclusion and an unambiguous placing of the tertiary hydroxyl group was achieved by Hardy and Rigby. By the oxidation of anhydromarrubiin Ghigi obtained a compound which the former workers interpreted as being the substance (CI), and this was confirmed by its spectral properties. Hydrolysis to the keto hydroxy acid and further oxidation then gave the diketo acid (CII). This was then oxidised with selenium dioxide to the conjugated enedione (CIII) which could be reduced back to the saturated diketo acid with zinc and acetic acid. The ultra-violet spectrum of the enedione ($\lambda_{max.}$ 242 mμ) showed that this was in a *cis*oid arrangement.

Although this work was consistent with the *seco*-pimarane structure no direct evidence of the carbon skeleton had been adduced. This was now obtained by Burn and Rigby (33). The starting ma-

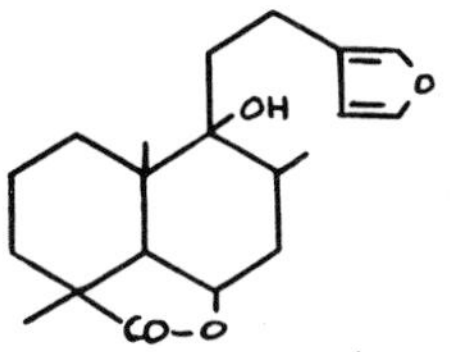

(XCV)

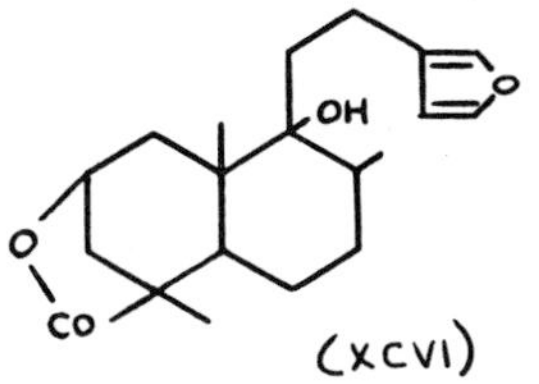

(XCVI)

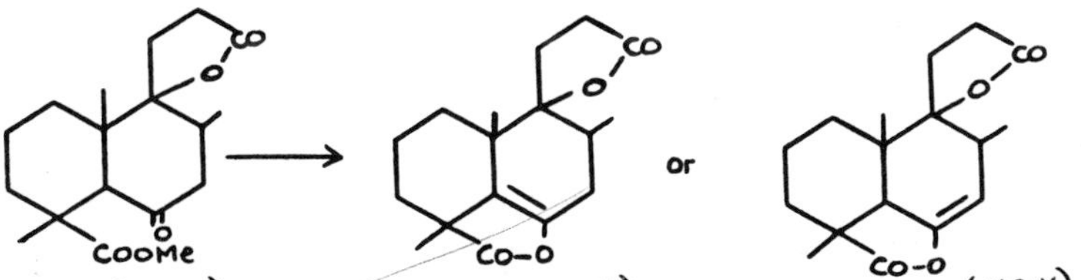

(XCVII) → (XCVIII) or (XCIX)

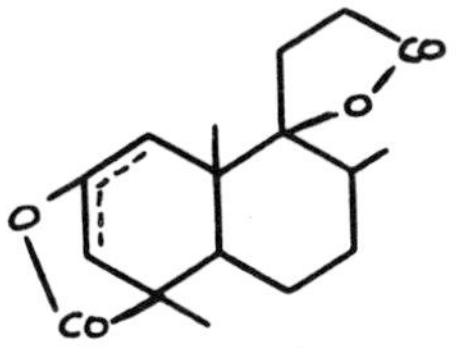

(C)

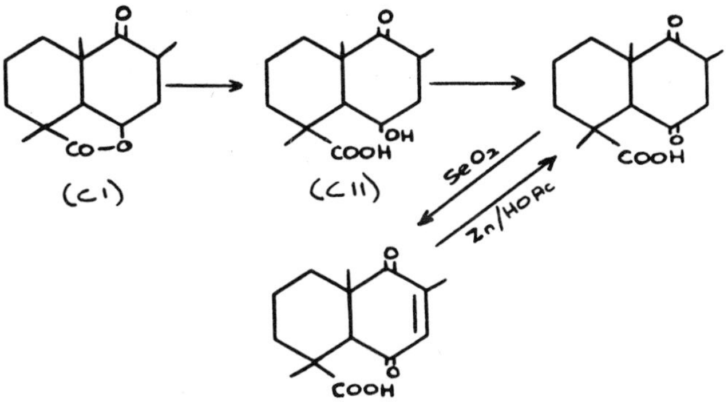

(CI) → (CII) → (by SeO₂ / Zn·HOAc)

(CIII)

terial was the enol lactone (XCIX) (the alternative structure (XCVIII) was later excluded by Cocker and his colleagues by ozonolysis to (CIV) and characterisation of the crystalline product as an aldehyde by a positive Schiff and Tollens test), and the final product (CVI) of this series of reactions from (XCIX) was a product of known structure and stereochemistry derived from ambrein (page 72). This unsaturated acid is obtained by the opening of the lactone in ambreinolide with strong acid (34).   The formation of (CVI) from (CV), even under the vigorous conditions of the Wolff-Kishner, is remarkable.

This combined evidence, therefore, establishes marrubiin un-equivocally as (XCV). Apart from those stereochemical features incorporated in formula (CVI) the question of the stereochemistry of marrubiin has not been settled.

One further aspect of marrubiin chemistry is of interest.   Ghigi

(CIV)   (XCIX)   COOH

(CV)   (CVI)

has shown that on further oxidation of the acid (CVII) corresponding to the ester (XCVII) with permanganate in strongly alkaline solution two neutral compounds were obtained. The nature of these products has now been resolved (32) (33). Using sulphur dioxide in the working up of the oxidation, Cocker and his co-workers obtained a ketohydroxy acid, $C_{17}H_{24}O_6$. This compound (33) merely lactonises on heating so that the simplest structure (CVIII) is untenable. By the process shown, however, this is converted into the isomeric (CIX) with concomitant lactonisation. The other lactone, however, remains open. The dilactone obtained on melting, or on acid treatment, is then (CX). This dilactone is one of the substances isolated by Ghigi using hydrochloric acid instead of sulphur dioxide in the working up process. On treatment with alkali both the dilactone and the keto hydroxy acid (CIX) are decarboxylated, (β-keto acids) and two products may be obtained one of which, the more stable, is the second of the compounds isolated by Ghigi. This may be (CXI); the other has been suggested to be one of the tautomers (CXII) or (CXIII). This presumably requires a conformational change in the seven-membered ring preceding its contraction (35).

Cafestol, $C_{20}H_{28}O_3$, is the main constituent of the unsaponifiable matter in the coffee-bean oil. From the outset great difficulty was experienced in purification because of the occurrence together with it of a more unsaturated compound, kahweol. The latter is very sensitive to light, air, heat, and acid and is responsible for a band at 290 mμ in the spectrum of most specimens of cafestol. Cafestol was the subject of extensive investigation between about 1940 and 1945 at which time it was believed that cafestol had oestrogenic activity. This also led to the proposal of steroid type formulae. The steroid concept was abandoned when the oestrogenic activity of cafestol was disproved. During this time Wettstein and his collaborators (39) had accumulated a good deal of information without, however, being able to advance structures. The conclusion was reached that cafestol was very probably diterpenoid. A further difficulty was the non-production, at this stage, of recognisable dehydrogenation products.

The available results may be summarised as follows. Two of the oxygen atoms are present as hydroxyl groups one of which is pri-

(CVII) (CVIII)

(CX) (CIX)

(CXIII) (CXII) (CXI)

mary and the other tertiary. Furthermore these are present in an α-glycol system of the type $> C(OH) \cdot CH_2OH$ since distillation of cafestol or its acetate with zinc dust gave the aldehyde $> CH \cdot CHO$. More satisfactory evidence for this was found when it was shown (39) that with lead tetraacetate a compound epoxynorcafestadienone, $C_{19}H_{24}O_2$, was obtained by cleavage of the α-glycol to give a ketone. Hydrogenation experiments as well as per acid titrations showed the presence of two double bonds. These were conjugated and cisoid since a maleic anhydride adduct was obtained. Since cafestol has a maximum at 225 mμ (the band at longer wavelengths being due to kahweol) this is very suggestive of a furan ring and such a system was postulated at a fairly early stage. The incorporation of a furan moiety into the structure was favoured by Wettstein because of the sensitivity of cafestol to acids and oxidation. Some further evidence was adduced by Wettstein for the size of the ring containing the carbonyl group in epoxynorcafestadienone. The ketone similarly derived from tetrahydrocafestol gave with potassium hypoiodite a dicarboxylic acid, $C_{19}H_{28}O_5$, which gave an anhydride, thus suggesting a five-membered ketone. One of the carboxyls of the dicarboxylic acid was hindered and was probably tertiary. The size of the ring in the ketone was subsequently confirmed by Djerassi and his colleagues (37) from infra-red data (band at 1742 cm^{-1}). These results may be summed up in the partial formula (CXIV) and the transformation shown.

The furan ring in epoxynorcafestadienone was believed by Wettstein to be attached to the rest of the molecule by juncture at positions 2 and 3, as in (CXV). Ozonolysis of this compound gave a keto dicarboxylic acid and two molecules of carbon dioxide. This dicarboxylic acid gave on pyrolysis a diketone and so it was deduced that the ring adjoining the furan was six- or seven-membered. It was shown to be six-membered (37) later from infra-red data (bands at 1744 and 1737 cm^{-1}) of the diketone, both of the rings containing the carbonyl groups being five-membered. This sequence may be represented as shown opposite. Since one of the carboxyl groups in the ketodicarboxylic acid is very hindered, it was very probable that

(CXIV)

(CXV)

a hydrogen atom was *not* present at one of the positions marked with
an asterisk in (CXV). Oxidation of cafestol with chromic acid gave
hydroxyketonorcafestenolide also obtained from epoxynorcafestadienone by the action of monoperphthalic acid. This is analogous to
the oxidation product obtained from menthofuran, and as regards the
furan moiety is represented by the change (CXV) → (CXVI). This
compound, again paralleling the menthofuran oxidation product,
could be dehydrated and gave a substance with the part structure
(CXVII). The conclusion drawn, therefore, is that α to this hydroxyl
there must be at least one hydrogen atom. The position lacking a
hydrogen must then be the other asterisked point, and (CXV) may
thus be expanded to (CXVIII) (36). The diketone condensed with
m-nitrobenzaldehyde whereas epoxynorcafestadienone did not, and
so *two* hydrogens, as in (CXIX), must be present β to the furan
oxygen. A major advance was made (37) when a dehydrogenation
product was finally isolated. Treatment of epoxynorcafestadienone
with hypoiodite gave, as in the case of the tetrahydro derivative already mentioned, a dicarboxylic acid by cleavage of the ring at the
carbonyl group. Dehydrogenation of this with palladium catalyst
gave a phenanthrol recognised by spectral data and identified later
by synthesis as (CXX). This oxygen atom and the ethyl substituent
mark the position of the furan ring, and so the part formula for
cafestol may be expanded to (CXXI).

It now remains to attach the four remaining carbon atoms one of
which was part of a primary alcoholic group. The ring to be formed
by this addition is five-membered, as already shown, and may be
attached by 1:2 or 1:3 bonds to the nucleus. If the junction is
1:2 then all the remaining carbon atoms are necessary to the formation of a five-membered ring, whereas with a 1:3 junction one carbon atom, as methyl group, remains to be placed. The spectrum of
epoxy*nor*cafestadiene (obtained by Wolff-Kishner reduction of the
dienone) was examined and exhibited a band at 1384 cm^{-1} attributa-
ble to a methyl group. The five-membered ring was therefore to be
formed by 1:3 addition to the nucleus. Of these Djerassi and his
colleagues preferred that shown in (CXXII) partly because of its
biogenetic relationship to phyllocladene. The glycol system was
placed at C_{15} and not at C_{16} also because the derived ketone gave

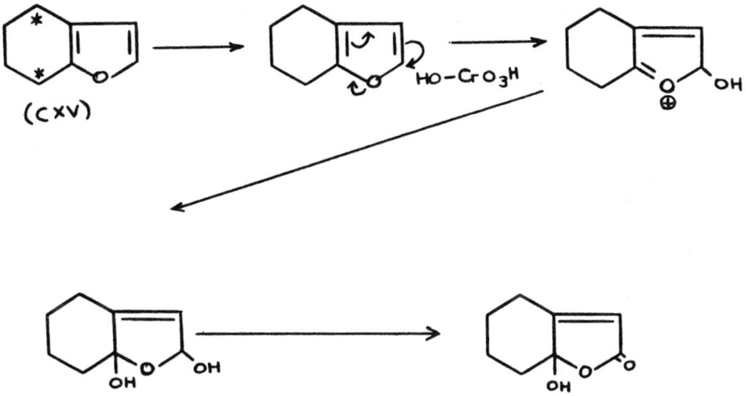

(CXV)

HO–CrO₃H

OH

OH   (CXVI)

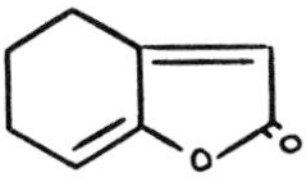

(CXVII) 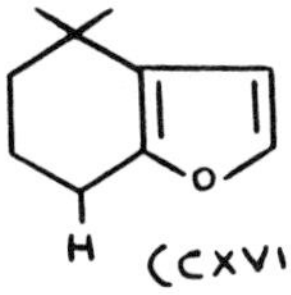   (CXVIII) 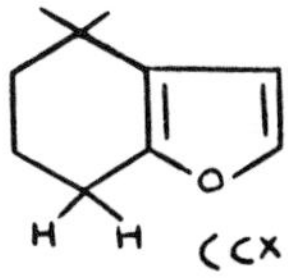   (CXIX)

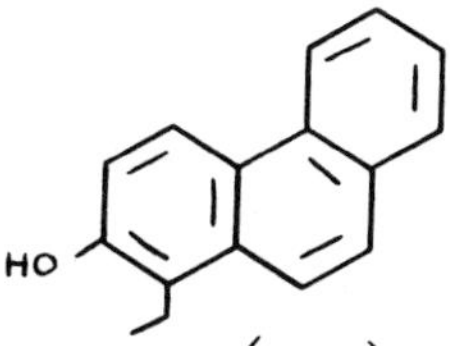

HO   (CXX)

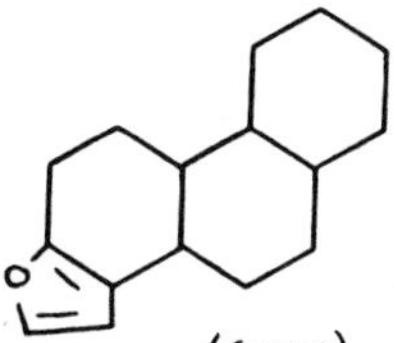

(CXXI)

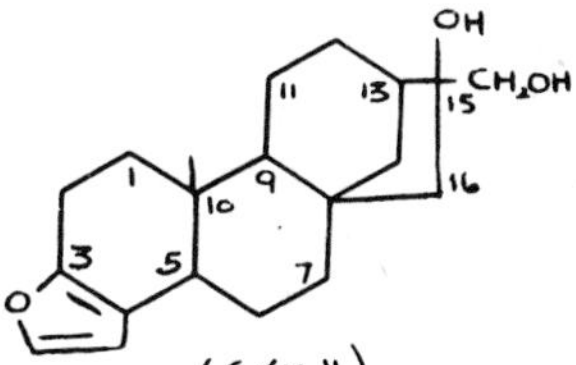

(CXXII)

(36) a tribromo derivative. Since, however, the ketone is at a bridgehead this last point is not persuasive.

It was pointed out then by Haworth and his colleagues (36) that the formulation (CXXII) did not contain the partial function (CXIX) which they had deduced to be present. They therefore preferred the structure (CXXIII), differing in the position of a methyl group. This was supported by the conversion of cafestol by a three-stage oxidation process to a tetracarboxylic acid, presumed to be (CXXIV), which on dehydrogenation with selenium gave (CXXV) and (CXXVI), both identified by comparison with authentic specimens.

Stevioside was first isolated by Rasenak in 1904. It is obtained from a small wild shrub growing in Paraguay known as kaá nê-ê (*Stevia rebaudiana* Bertoni). The leaves of this plant are very sweet, and stevioside is the agent responsible for this. The pure glycoside is, in fact, about three hundred times sweeter than sugar; it appears to be the sweetest known naturally occurring substance. It can be hydrolysed with acid to give a crystalline aglycone with D-glucose as the only sugar component. It may also be hydrolysed by the digestive juice or hepato-pancreatic juice of the snail *Helix pomatia*. In this case glucose was again liberated, but the aglycone differed from, yet was isomeric with, the substance obtained by acid hydrolysis. That liberated by enzymes was presumed the true aglycone and was named steviol. Acid treatment of this converted it into *iso*steviol, the isomer.

The yield of glucose indicated that three glucose residues were present in stevioside. The mode of combination of these was resolved (40) by the use of modern techniques. Methylation, followed by hydrolysis and paper chromatography, gave two sugar products, one present in twice the proportion of the other. This, together with the consumption of five moles of periodate (giving two moles formic acid), suggested that the three glucose units were not linked separately to the aglycone. This was confirmed when it was found that, surprisingly, base hydrolysis gave one mole of sugar as levoglucosan (CXXVII), and a new glycoside, steviobioside. This glycoside contained a hindered carboxyl group not present in the original glycoside. It was also not sweet. The liberation of the sugar with base therefore suggested that one glycopyranose must be attached

(CXXIII)

(CXXIV)

(CXXV)

(CXXVI)

as an ester. Since steviol has the formula $C_{20}H_{30}O_3$ only one oxygen atom remains by which the remaining sugar residues may be attached. Steviobioside consumed three molecules of lead tetraacetate; by methylation and acid hydrolysis $2:3:4:6$-tetramethyl- and $3:4:6$-trimethyl-O-methyl-D-glucose were obtained. The glucose residues were, therefore, attached through a C_2 link as shown in (CXXVIII). These are comparatively rare in nature. The occurrence of sugar esters of this type is apparently also rare. The formation of the levoglucosan (CXXVI) presumably involves alkyl-oxygen fission as occurs in aryl-β-D-glucopyranosides (41).

Steviol contains one double bond present as an *exo* methylene group. *Iso*steviol, on the other hand does not have this feature. Furthermore, the hydroxyl group present in steviol is not present in *iso*steviol but is replaced by a carbonyl group. This transformation is similar to that encountered in the diterpenoid alkaloids such as laurifoline; the change may be represented by the partial formula (CXXIX) → (CXXX). Since dehydrogenation of *iso*steviol gives pimanthrene a structure (CXXXI), analogous to that of phyllocladene, has been proposed for steviol; it is not rigidly established.

Colombo root (*Jatrorrhiza palmata* Miers) contains a number of bitter principles. The structure of one of these, columbin, has recently been established (42) and is probably the most complex and subtle of the diterpenoids so far encountered. This may be judged by the fact that although extensive investigation had previously been carried out by other workers, notably Wessely and Feist and their respective collaborators, at the time of the investigation by Barton and Elad agreement had not been reached even as to the nature of the functional groups.

Columbin has the formula $C_{20}H_{22}O_6$. On mild treatment with alkali it is converted into an isomer, *iso*columbin. Also, with alkali both substances behave as dilactones; four of the six oxygen atoms are thus accounted for. With acetic anhydride–sodium acetate both columbin and *iso*columbin give the same monoacetate (not obtained with pyridine–acetic anhydride) and on methylation with dimethyl sulphate and alkali both substances give the same monomethyl ether. This hydroxyl group does not, however, give acidic reactions. The remaining oxygen atom is inert.

(CXX VIII)

(CXX VII)

(CXXIX)

(CXXX)

(CXXXI)

An important feature of the chemistry of columbin is the ready decarboxylation to decarboxycolumbin. Furthermore, although decarboxycolumbin cannot be acetylated or methylated, *iso*columbin acetate and *O*-methyl*iso*columbin both lose one molecule of carbon dioxide at the melting point. As would be expected, the carbon dioxide has come from a lactone group since the dicarboxy derivatives titrate now as monolactones. A number of systems including, for instance, β-lactones, are known which lose carbon dioxide on heating to the melting point, but few of these accommodate the relevant requirements. One further experimental fact stringently limits the possibilities, namely, that columbin readily decarboxylates, whereas dihydrocolumbin (42), prepared by hydrogenation over palladised calcium carbonate, does not. This was rationalised by Barton and Elad in the partial formula (CXXXII). If R = H, as in columbin, the product is (CXXXIII), which now contains a carbonyl group. If R = Ac or Me, then the product is (CXXXIV), an enol ether or acetate. It will be noted in (CXXXII) that the transition state appears to constitute a contravention of Bredt's rule. This particular instance is analogous to the decarboxylation of (CXXXV) (43).

The partial formula (CXXXII) contains three of the columbin oxygen atoms. There remains one lactone and the inert oxygen. The empirical formula of columbin requires a total of ten double bond equivalents. If it is bicyclic then so far they have been disposed as follows: two for the bicyclic skeleton; two each for the lactone rings (one for the ring and one for the carbonyl) and one for the ethylenic linkage in (CXXXII), making a total of seven. Three thus remain. Two of these were presumed ethylenic linkages because more vigorous hydrogenation of columbin gave octahydro derivatives in which, however, hydrogenolysis has taken place because the products from columbin and *iso*columbin are lactonic acids.

These two ethylenic linkages, the inert oxygen and the remaining double bond equivalent, were believed to be combined as a furan, and there was ultra-violet and infra-red evidence to support this. Confirmation was obtained by ozonolysis of dihydrocolumbin when the major product was a C_{17} acid. This corresponds to the con-

(CXXXII)   (CXXXIV)   (CXXXIII)   (CXXXV)

version of (CXXXVI) to (CXXXVII). Since only formic acid could
be detected as a volatile acid this supported the contention that
there was no alkyl substituent in the furan ring. The partial formula
(CXXXVI) could. be expanded for the following reasons. Of the two
lactones in columbin one is reversibly opened with alkali and the
other is not. The remaining lactone in decarboxycolumbin is also
reversibly opened. Hydrogenolysis requires, in general, allylic or
vinylic attachment to a double bond. In this case vinylic attachment can be excluded since alkali-catalysed opening would lead
to an unstable enol. Now since reduction of the double bond in
(CXXXII) precedes hydrogenolysis it follows that it is the *other*
lactone which is both reversibly opened with alkali and is α to an
ethylenic linkage. The ethylenic linkage concerned in this case
will be that of the furan ring. (CXXXVI) may thus be expanded to
(CXXXVIII).

This summarises briefly the evidence available for characterisation of the functional groups of columbin. Previous work directed
to the elucidation of the carbon skeleton was not simply rationalised.
Zinc distillation of columbin gave o-cresol and $1:2:5$-trimethyl
naphthalene (CXXXIX). Fusion with potassium hydroxide gave
$2:4$-dimethylbenzoic acid (CXL) and 2-methylterephthalic acid
(CXLI). Oxidation with manganese dioxide and sulphuric acid gave
(CXLII) and (CXLIII). This evidence suggested the bicyclic nucleus was substituted as in (CXXXIX). Hydrogenation of decarboxycolumbin gave, with hydrogenolysis, decarboxyoctahydrocolumbinic
acid. Reduction of this with lithium aluminium hydride and dehydrogenation again gave (CXXXIX). With the object, now, of locating
the carbonyl group of the lactone in (CXXXII) the hydrogenolysis
product of columbin, octahydrocolumbinic acid, was also reduced
with lithium aluminium hydride. Dehydrogenation of this, however,
only gave (CXXXIX). Since the particular carbon atom which it
was intended to retain is not attached to a quaternary carbon atom
it should not have been eliminated; the only alternative is that one
of the methyl groups in (CXXXIX) itself results from a migration
from an adjacent quaternary position. This is similar to a $1:2$
shift of the Wagner kind taking place under the vigorous, and presumably acidic, conditions of selenium dehydrogenation. This was

R ——⟨furan⟩——→ R·COOH

(CXXXVI)   (CXXXVII)

R (CXXXVIII)

(CXXXIX)

(CXL)   (CXLI)

(CXLII)

(CXLIII)

confirmed as follows. Decarboxyoctahydrocolumbinic acid contains the function (CXXXIII). Wolff-Kishner reduction removed the carbonyl group, and selenium dehydrogenation then gave 1-methyl-2-naphthoic acid (CXLIV) in which no migration has occurred to give a substituent at C_5. On the other hand, reduction of the carbonyl to hydroxyl, giving decarboxydecahydrocolumbinic acid, and dehydrogenation gave (CXLV) in which methyl migration *has* taken place. Migration, as expected, therefore only takes place when an oxygen function is present to provide by elimination, a carbonium ion. From this it was concluded that a methyl group was present α to the lactone carbonyl and that the lactone carbonyl was attached at C_5 (naphthalene numbering). This gives, for columbin, the partial formula (CXLVI). The position of the side-chain bearing the furan ring is marked by the methyl group in (CXLIV), whilst the position of the second lactone is marked by the carboxyl group in the same compound. The other end of the second lactone terminates α to the furan ring. Two possibilities were then present: either columbin has a δ- and a γ-lactone, in which case it was represented by partial formula (CXLVII), or it had two γ-lactones, and was represented by (CXLVIII). The side-chain in (CXLVII) resembles that of marrubiin. It was established by Kuhn-Roth determination and quantitative infra-red measurements of the 1380 cm^{-1} C—Me band that columbin contained two C—Me groups; (CXLVII) was therefore correct. It was not found possible to differentiate between lactone sizes directly on the basis of infra-red spectra. The angular methyl group to be added to (CXLVII) may be placed at two points giving (CXLIX) or (CL). (CL) was preferred as accounting better for the formation of o-cresol, (CXL), and (CXLI) on vigorous degradation. The remaining point, the change from columbin to *iso*columbin, is interpreted as epimerisation at the carbon atom α to the carbonyl group.

(CXLIV)

(CXLV)

(CXLVI)

(CXLVII)

(CXLVIII)

(CXLIX)

(CL)

REFERENCES

1. Vesterberg, A., *Ber.,* **36,** 4200 (1903).
2. Bamberger, E., and S. C. Hooker, *Ber..* **18,** 1024, 1030, 1750 (1885); Bamberger, E., and S. C. Hooker, *Ann.,* **229,** 102 (1885).
3. Bucher, J. E., *J. Am. Chem. Soc.,* **32,** 374 (1910).
4. Ruzicka, L., J. Meyer, and M. Pfeiffer, *Helv. Chim. Acta,* **8,** 637 (1925); Ruzicka, L., M. W. Goldberg, H. W. Huyser, and C. F. Seidel, *Helv. Chim. Acta,* **14,** 545 (1931).
5. Ruzicka, L., and J. Meyer, *Helv. Chim. Acta,* **5,** 581, (1922).
6. Ruzicka, L., G. B. R. de Graaff, and J. R. Hosking, *Helv. Chim. Acta,* **14,** 233 (1931); Ruzicka, L., G. B. R. de Graaff, and H. J. Muller, *Helv. Chim. Acta,* **15,** 1300 (1932).
7. Haworth, R. D., *J. Chem. Soc.,* **1932,** 2717.
8. Barton, D. H. R., *Chem. & Ind. (London),* **1948,** 638.
9. Subluskey, L. A., and T. F. Sanderson, *J. Am. Chem. Soc.,* **76,** 3512 (1954); Velluz, L., G. Muller, A. Petit, and J. Mathieu, *Bull. soc. chim. France,* **1954,** 401.
10. Barton, D. H. R., *Quart. Rev.,* **3,** 36 (1949).
11. Klyne, W., *J. Chem. Soc.,* **1953,** 3072.
12. Heusser, H., E. Beriger, R. Anliker, O. Jeger, and L. Ruzicka, *Helv. Chim. Acta,* **36,** 1918 (1953).
13. Stork, G., and J. W. Schulenberg, *J. Am. Chem. Soc.,* **78,** 250 (1956).
14. Stork, G., R. Terrell, and J. Szmuskovicz, *J. Am. Chem. Soc.,* **76,** 2029 (1954).
15. Harris, G. C., and T. F. Sanderson, *J. Am. Chem. Soc.,* **70,** 339 (1948).
16. Wenkert, E., *Chem. & Ind. (London),* **1955,** 282.
17. King, F. E., and G. Jones, *J. Chem. Soc.,* **1955,** 658.
18. Zeiss, H. H., and F. W. Grant, *J. Am. Chem. Soc.,* **79,** 1201 (1957).
19. Petru, F., and V. Galik, *Collection Czechoslov. Chem. Communs.,* **18,** 717 (1953).
20. Campbell, W. P., and D. Todd, *J. Am. Chem. Soc.,* **79,** 573 (1957).
21. King, F. E., T. J. King, and J. G. Topliss, *J. Chem. Soc.,* **1957,** 573.
22. Cocker, J. D., and T. G. Halsall, *J. Chem. Soc.,* **1956,** 4262.
23. King, F. E., T. J. King, and J. G. Topliss, *Chem. & Ind. (London),* **1956,** 133.
24. King, F. E., T. J. King, and K. G. Neill, *J. Chem. Soc.,* **1953,** 1055; King, F. E., and T. J. King, *J. Chem. Soc.,* **1953,** 4158.
25. King, F. E., D. H. Godson, and T. J. King, *J. Chem. Soc.,* **1955,** 1117.
26. Hosking, J. R., and C. W. Brandt, *Ber.,* **67,** 1173 (1934), **68,** 37, 286, 1311 (1935), **69,** 780 (1936).
27. (a) Short, W. F., and H. Wang, *J. Chem. Soc.,* **1951,** 2979; cf. Brandt, C. W., and B. R. Thomas, *New Zealand J. Sci. Technol.,* **B33,** 30 (1951). (b) Barltrop, J. A., and N. A. J. Rogers, *Chem. & Ind. (London),* **1957,** 397.

28. Brandt, C. W., *New Zealand J. Sci. Technol.*, **34B**, 46 (1952).
29. Fischer, F. G., *Ann.*, **464**, 69 (1928); Fischer, F. G., and K. Lowenburg, *Ann.* **475**, 183 (1929); cf. also Smith, L. I., and J. A. Spring, *J. Am. Chem. Soc.*, **65**, 1276 (1943); Karrer, P., A. Geiger, H. Rentschler, E. Zbinden, and A. Kugler, *Helv. Chim. Acta*, **26**, 1741 (1943).
30. Gordin, H. M., *J. Am. Chem. Soc.*, **30**, 265 (1908); Lawson, A., and E. D. Eustice, *J. Chem. Soc.*, **1939**, 587; Hollis, F., J. H. Richards, and A. Robertson, *Nature*, **143**, 604 (1939).
31. Ghigi, E., *Gazz. chim. ital.*, **78**, 865 (1948); *81*, 336 (1951); **83**, 252 (1953); and other papers in this series.
32. Cocker, W., B. E. Cross, S. R. Duff, and T. F. Holley, *Chem. & Ind. (London)*, **1952**, 827; Cocker W., B. E. Cross, S. R. Duff, J. T. Edward, and T. F. Holley, *J. Chem. Soc.*, **1953**, 2540; Cocker, W., J. T. Edward, T. F. Holley, and D. M. S. Wheeler, *Chem. & Ind. (London)*, **1955**, 1485.
33. Hardy, D. G., and W. Rigby, *Chem. & Ind. (London)*, **1953**, 1150; Burn, D., and W. Rigby, *Chem. & Ind. (London)*, **1953**, 386; Burn, D., D. P. Moody, and W. Rigby, *Chem. & Ind. (London)*, **1956**, 928.
34. Sorm, F., M. Suchy, and V. Herout, *Collection Czechoslov. Chem. Communs.*, **16**, 278 (1951).
35. Jones, D. N., J. R. Lewis, C. W. Shoppee, and G. H. R. Summers, *J. Chem. Soc.*, **1955**, 2876.
36. Haworth, R. D., A. H. Jubb, and J. McKenna, *J. Chem. Soc.*, **1955**, 1983; Haworth, R. D., and R. A. W. Johnstone, *J. Chem. Soc.*, **1957**, 1492.
37. Djerassi, C., E. Wilfred, L. Visco, and A. J. Lemin, *J. Org. Chem.*, **18**, 1449 (1953); Djerassi C., H. Bendas, and P. Sengupta, *J. Org. Chem.*, **20**, 1046 (1955); *Chem. & Ind.* (London), **1955**, 1481.
38. Ruzicka, L., and H. Waldmann, *Helv. Chim. Acta*, **18**, 611 (1935); Crowfoot, D., *J. Chem. Soc.*, **1938**, 1241.
39. Wettstein, A., M. Spillmann, and K. Miescher, *Helv. Chim. Acta*, **28**, 1004 (1945); and previous papers in this series.
40. Wood, H. B., R. Allerton, H. W. Diehl, and H. G. Fletcher, *J. Org. Chem.*, **20**, 875 (1955); Mosettig, E., and W, R. Nes, *J. Org. Chem.*, **20**, 884 (1955).
41. McCloskey, C. M., and G. H. Coleman, *J. Org. Chem.*, **10**, 184 (1945); Lemieux, R. V., and C. Brice, *Can. J. Chem.* **30**, 295 (1952).
42. Barton, D. H. R., and D. Elad, *J. Chem. Soc.*, **1956**, 2085, 2090; Cava, M. P., and E. J. Soboczenski, *J. Am. Chem. Soc.*, **78**, 5317 (1956).
43. Diels, O., and K. Alder, *Ann.*, **490**, 257 (1931).
44. Ruzicka, L., and E. Bernold, *Helv. Chim. Acta*, **24**, 931, 1167 (1941); Ruzicka, L., and E. Rey, *Helv. Chim. Acta*, **26**, 2136 (1943); and previous papers in this series.

CHAPTER 2

THE TRITERPENOIDS: I

The triterpenoids constitute by far the largest terpenoid class. They have been known and investigated for over 100 years, but it is only within the last 25 years that serious progress has been made towards the elucidation of their structures. They are widely distributed in nature, for the most part in the vegetable kingdom. Amongst the exceptions are the hydrocarbon squalene, first obtained from shark liver oil, ambrein from ambergris, and a number of tetracyclic substances isolated from wool fat. The latter substances, including lanosterol, have structures which do not conform to the isoprene rule, and in fact may be considered to be trimethyl steroids. Since their reactions are closely allied to those of the triterpenoids they are included here.

The triterpenoids occur in the plant kingdom as esters, as glycosides, or in the free state. Few of the glycosides have been obtained pure or have been adequately characterised. The sugar moieties include pentoses, such as arabinose, xylose, and rhamnose, and hexoses such as glucose, fructose, and galactose. Units of glucuronic or galacturonic acid may also be included. The saponins are water-soluble and lower surface tension, and are used for their foaming properties. A few of the better characterised saponins are given in Table 1.

TABLE 1

Triterpenoid Saponins

Saponin	Source	Sapogenin	Sugar
Asiaticoside	*Centella asiatica*	Asiatic acid	Glucose, rhamnose
Cyclamin	*Cyclamen europaeum*	Cyclamiretin	Glucose, arabinose
Aescin	Horse chestnuts	Aescigenin	Glucose, galactose, glucuronic acid, etc.
α-Hederin	Ivy leaves	Hederagenin	Fructose, arabinose, rhamnose
Quinovin	Cinchona bark	Quinovic acid	D-Quinovose (*iso*rhodeose)
Soapnut saponin	*Sapindus* spp.	Hederagenin	Fructose, arabinose, rhamnose
Sugar beet saponin	Sugar beet	Oleanolic acid	Glucuronic acid

The triterpenoids may be classified into three groups as follows: (a) ambrein and squalene, (b) the tetracyclic triterpenoids, and (c) the pentacyclic triterpenoids. The first group, as mentioned, consists of only two substances. The second group consists of the so-called methylated steroids. Here also are included a number of substances which contain 31 carbon atoms because they bear the same relationship to the ergostane series as do the C_{30} compounds to the cholestanes. The third group is by far the largest and is itself normally divided into three further sub-groups. These are: the α-amyrin group, the β-amyrin group, and the lupeol group. This division is, however, somewhat arbitrary. It arose when full structures were not known and substances were related to the simplest alcohol with the same skeleton. Since then, the full structures have been elucidated and still more recently conversions from one group into another have been accomplished. It is now believed (see Chapter 5) that there may be a single biogenetic scheme for all these triterpenoids with thirty carbon atoms with squalene (or its equivalent) as progenitor. In fact, since the promulgation of the theory, two predictable, but then unknown, skeletal structures have been found in nature.

The division of the triterpenoids into classes is, in this view, without much significance. It will be adhered to because of its convenience in discussing the chemistry within the groups.

The difficulties which were encountered in the structural work on the triterpenoids were very considerable. With this work and much of the brilliant achievement thereof must be associated the name of Leopold Ruzicka. These difficulties were manifold. Functional groups, through which degradation and opening of the molecule could be achieved, were either at one remote end of the molecule or, if they happened to be situated in the centre, unreactive.

The method of sulphur dehydrogenation used with such success by Ruzicka on the sesquiterpenoids, when applied to the triterpenoids, resulted in disruption of the molecule. The products were largely naphthalenic fragments. However, from a study of these and of certain pyrolytic reactions (which resulted in a cleavage of the molecule into isolable portions) a vast body of evidence was built up, which finally enabled the deduction of the complex structures.

It may be mentioned that the mass spectrometer (1) can render useful service here since accurate molecular weight may be obtained which distinguishes readily between C_{30} and C_{31} substances, a process difficult on the basis of mere carbon and hydrogen analysis. By this technique also, the side-chain, if any, may be cleaved in one piece, and its molecular weight determined.

SQUALENE

As already mentioned squalene was first isolated from the liver oils of sharks. Soon after it was found in other fish oils and in the oils from sharks eggs. Since then it has been realised that its distribution in nature is, in smaller amounts, far more widespread than had been imagined. It has been isolated from such varied sources as fungi, human ear wax, and hair oil.

Until 1930 the results of chemical investigation had revealed that squalene probably contained six double bonds, was acyclic, and gave crystalline hexahydrobromides and hydrochlorides. There was some doubt about the homogeneity of the derivatives and considerable doubt about that of the hydrocarbon itself. Much of this dubiety was resolved by the careful investigations of Heilbron and his colleagues (2). The gross constitution of squalene was proven by Karrer and Helfenstein (3) when they synthesised, by the action of sodium or magnesium on farnesyl bromide (II), a hydrocarbon giving the same two hexahydrochlorides (separated by fractional crystallisation) as given by natural squalene. No conclusions regarding geometrical isomerism could be drawn, since in any case the farnesyl bromide was inhomogeneous. It has, in fact, been shown by Dauben and Bradlow (4), by the use of deuterium, that synthetic squalene contains *exo* methylene groups. Furthermore, the hydrocarbon recovered from the hydrochlorides is not squalene, but is probably a mixture of some of the more than a thousand possible isomers.

Two problems had to be solved before the stereospecific synthesis of natural squalene could be attempted. Firstly, it was necessary to know its geometry. Evidence was eventually provided by X-ray diffraction measurements of the thiourea adducts that squalene

is the all-*trans* isomer represented in (I) (5). The second difficulty was that of a criterion of identity. Infra-red spectroscopy was not found sufficiently sensitive, and the method finally adopted was the following. It was known (Chapter 5) that squalene could be converted enzymatically into lanosterol. This reaction is, as are most enzymic processes, stereospecific; the squalene recovered by the hydrochloride is, for instance, inactive.

With these problems solved, the synthesis of squalene was attempted by two groups (6,7) using a similar route. This involved the use of the Wittig reagent prepared from 1:4-dibromobutane and triphenylphosphine (8). In general the Wittig reaction is that between a triphenylalkylphosphorus ylide of the general formula

$$(C_6H_5)_3 \overset{\oplus}{P} \!-\!\!-\! \overset{\ominus}{CHR}$$

and a carbonyl group, $R_1R_2 \cdot CO$, when the oxygen of the carbonyl group is replaced by the alkyl moiety of the reagent to give $R_1R_2C \!=\! CHR$. In the present case the reagent was reacted with homogeneous *trans*-geranylacetone (III). The hydrocarbon obtained (consisting of a mixture of geometrical isomers about the double bond formed in the reaction) was then purified through the thiourea adduct. The final product was the *trans* isomer because the *cis* isomer has not dimensions suitable for the formation of a stable clathrate (9). The hydrocarbon was spectroscopically indistinguishable from natural squalene, and has been reported to be enzymically active.

AMBREIN

Ambrein is a tricyclic tertiary alcohol, first isolated in 1820, which is obtained from ambergris. The structural investigations took advantage of the fact that under quite mild oxidative conditions the molecule could be broken into two main fragments.

After the empirical formula $C_{30}H_{52}O$ had been established (10) it was shown, by peracid titrations and by the preparation of a saturated tetrahydroambrein, that ambrein contained two double bonds. Since ambrein could be readily dehydrated to a hydrocarbon, ambra-

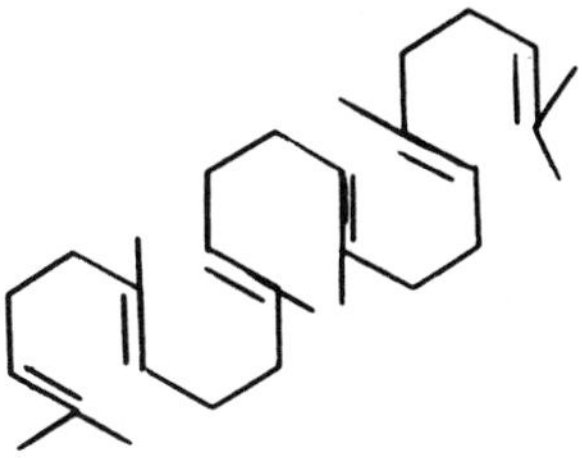

CH₂Br

(I)

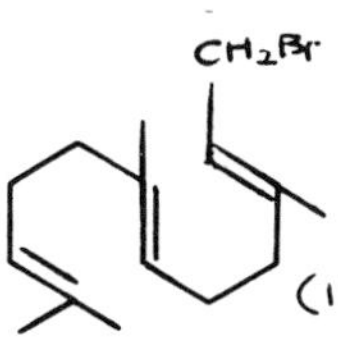

(II)

2.

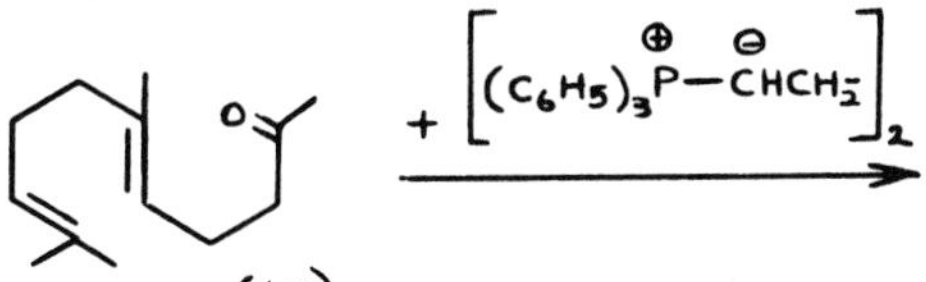

(III)

$+ \left[(C_6H_5)_3 \overset{\oplus}{P} - \overset{\ominus}{C}HCH_3 \right]_2$

(I)

triene, and because it could not be acetylated under normal conditions the oxygen function was presumed a tertiary alcohol. Ambrein was therefore tricyclic. Oxidation with ozone gave a lactone
$C_{17}H_{28}O_2$, a diketone $C_{12}H_{20}O_2$, and formic acid, all carbon atoms
being accounted for; the isolation of the formic acid strongly suggested the presence of an *exo* methylene group. The diketone (IV)
was shown to be a 1:5-diketone since it was readily cyclised by an
internal aldol condensation in the presence of base to a β-hydroxy
ketone. This could be dehydrated with acid to give (V), an $\alpha:\beta$-
unsaturated ketone; the structure (V) assigned was later confirmed
by synthesis. The lactone $C_{17}H_{28}O_2$ was attributed the structure
(VI). It was also obtained (11) from ambrein by permanganate oxidation accompanied, in this case, by dihydro-γ-ionone (VII). The
structure (VIII) for ambrein rested, then, on the structure assigned
to the lactone (VI) which was named ambreinolide. This was rigidly
confirmed in several ways. Treatment of ambreinolide with strong
acid gave the unsaturated acid (IX), which could in turn be hydrogenated to (X). The methyl ester of this, by reaction with phenylmagnesium bromide, gave a diphenylcarbinol which was dehydrated
and oxidised to give (XI) (Barbier-Wieland degradation). This acid

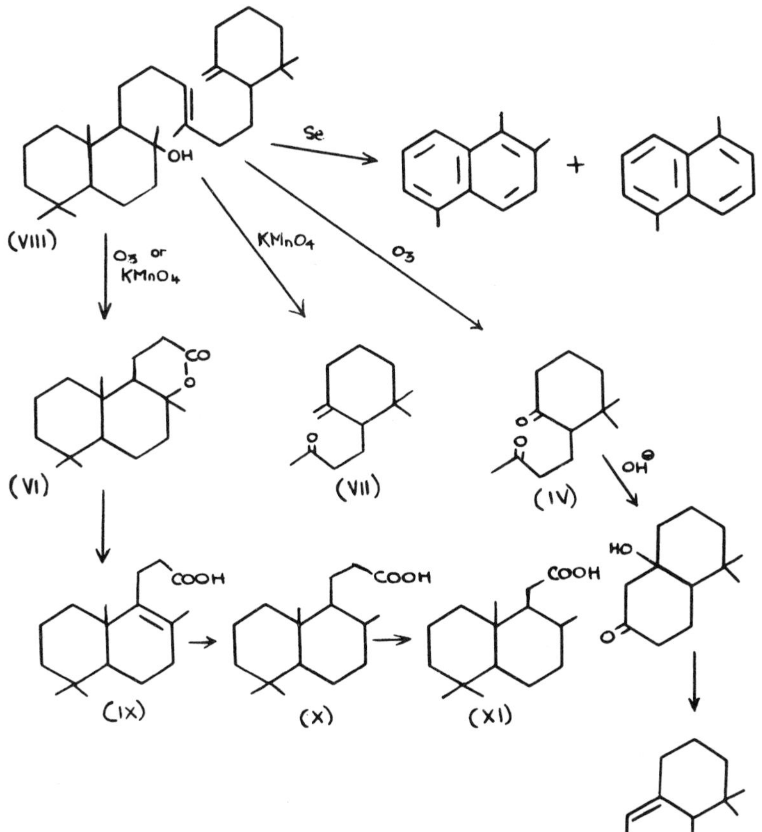

(VIII)
OH
Se
KMnO4
O3
O3 or
KMnO4
(VI)
CO
O
(VII)
(IV)
OH⊖
HO
COOH
(IX)
(X)
(XI)
(V)

had been previously obtained by oxidation of a derivative of manool, tetrahydromanoene (XII). This established the constitution of the carbon skeleton of ambreinolide, but did not distinguish between structures (VI) and (XIII). Decision was reached by examination of the minor products of permanganate oxidation. One of these was identical with a substance of known structure (XIV) obtained by the oxidation of sclareol. Further evidence was obtained by correlation with manool. This was achieved by oxidation of manool to (XV) followed by further conversion to ambreinolide (VI). Finally ambreinolide was synthesised by Dietrich and Lederer (12) from farnesyl bromide (II). The acid (XVI) was cyclised with formic acid to give DL-ambreinolide.

Amongst the acidic products obtained in the permanganate oxidation of ambrein was a hydroxy acid (XVII). This could be dehydrated with acid to give (XVIII) then hydrogenated to (XIX). The importance of this sequence of reactions lies in the fact that (XIX) was an acid previously obtained from oleanolic acid (page 138) and so establishes a relationship between ambrein and one group of the pentacyclic triterpenoids.

THE TETRACYCLIC TRITERPENOIDS

The tetracyclic triterpenoids are a group of substances which have been investigated only recently. An intensive effort by several groups of workers has elucidated the structures of some twenty of these compounds within the last five years. Most of the members of this group have a gross structural similarity but differ in certain major points of stereochemistry. This difference results in a remarkable divergence in chemical properties which can only be properly understood when the conformational aspects are also taken into account. The two main families in this group of compounds to which most others are related are represented in the two substances lanosterol and euphol, and these are accordingly dealt with in much more detail.

(XV) (XII) (XIV)

(XIII)

(II) → → (XVI) → (VI)

(XVII) → (XVIII) → (XIX)

THE LANOSTEROL GROUP

Lanosterol

The unsaponifiable fraction of wool fat contains cholesterol (XX) together with what was considered at one time to be another pure substance, "*iso*cholesterol." Later it was found that this was a complex mixture and it was shown by Ruzicka and his co-workers (13), by a prolonged and detailed fractional crystallisation and by the use of chromatography, that four substances were present. These were lanosterol (XXI), dihydrolanosterol (XXII), agnosterol (XXIII), and dihydroagnosterol (XXIV). Later it was shown that cryptosterol, a constituent of the yeast sterol mixture, was identical with lanosterol. Although previous work was of much assistance the structures of this group of substances was completely solved in the period 1949–1954 by Ruzicka and Jeger in Zurich, Barton in London, and McGhie, also in London, together with their collaborators.

Hydrogenation of lanosterol gives dihydrolanosterol (XXII) which still contains one double bond resistant to further hydrogenation. Since lanosterol has the composition $C_{30}H_{50}O$ and the oxygen is alcoholic it must, therefore, be tetracyclic. Some indication of the structure was given by the isolation of 1 : 2 : 8-trimethylphenanthrene (XXV) as the main product of selenium dehydrogenation. The alcohol was shown to be secondary by oxidation to a ketone, and its presence in a six-membered ring, with a methylene group flanking it, was shown by the series of reactions (XXVa) → (XXVb). Further

(XX)

(XXI)

(XXII)

(XXIII)

(XXIV)

(XXV)

(XXVa)   (XXVb)

indication was given by the reaction sequence (XXVc) → (XXVd), which was carried out on dihydrolanosterol. The first dehydration step is one encountered in other triterpenoids; for it to take the given course it is necessary that the oxygen atom, C_3, C_4, and C_5 be coplanar. Thereby the departure of the oxygen (presumably as a phosphorus chloroester) is facilitated by the approach of the electrons constituting the C_4-C_5 bond as illustrated in (XXVI). This requirement (anticipating the stereochemistry of the ring junction) implies that the hydroxyl in lanosterol is in the β (equatorial) configuration.

The environment of the easily hydrogenated double bond in lanosterol was shown by ozonolytic cleavage to give acetone; that of the inert double bond was deducted from a study of a large number of oxidation products. Infra-red spectral data suggested that it was tetrasubstituted, and this was confirmed when dihydrolanosteryl acetate (lanostenyl acetate) (XXVII) was oxidised with selenium dioxide, N-bromosuccinimide (NBS), or perbenzoic acid. A compound was obtained which had the characteristic ultra-violet absorption of a heteroannular diene as in (XXVIII). This substance was then identified as dihydroagnosteryl acetate. The conversion of (XXVII) to (XXVIII) presumably takes place as follows: with selenium dioxide either by allylic abstraction of hydrogen or by allylic hydroxylation and dehydration, with NBS by allylic bromination and dehydrobromination, and with the peracid through an epoxide followed by cleavage and dehydration.

The most characteristic oxidation product (XXIX) to be obtained from dihydrolanosterol derivatives (13) is that produced by the action of chromic acid. It contains the system — CO — C = C — CO — in a completely *trans*oid arrangement and may be recognised by its yellow colour, and by its ultra-violet and infra-red spectra. A characteristic of the enedione system, independent of its stereochemistry, is its reduction with zinc and acetic acid to the saturated diketone (xxVc) (xxVd)

(XXVI)

−H⊕

(XXVII) (XXVIII)

as in (XXX). The formation of (XXIX) required that the inert double bond be flanked by two methylene groups. Further, the infra-red data (band at 1697 cm^{-1}) of (XXX) indicated that the two carbonyl groups, in the flanking rings of the double bond were in six-membered rings, and hence implied the partial structure (XXXI). Oxidation of (XXIX) with selenium dioxide in boiling acetic acid gave (XXXII), further oxidised by the same reagent to (XXXIII). (XXXII) showed a band in the infra-red at 812 cm^{-1} indicating the formation of a triply substituted double bond, and (XXXIII) was shown to contain an α-diketone system by cleavage with alkaline hydrogen peroxide (14,15). The residual chromophore in (XXXIV) showed extended conjugation (λ_{max}. 251 mμ). The conclusions so far were supported by the production of (XXXV) by the selenium dioxide oxidation of dihydrolanosteryl (lanostenyl) acetate, and its further oxidation by chromic acid to (XXXIII). The compound (XXXIII) gave no indication of enolisation and resisted further oxidation. This suggested that no carbon atom α to the chromophore bore a hydrogen atom. This requires the partial formula (XXXVI) for dihydrolanosterol (lanostenol).

The next problem was to distinguish between the alternative possibilities that the two rings in (XXXVI) were B and C or C and D. The fact that so many quaternary carbon atoms were α to the chromophore strongly favoured the B/C formulation. Proof of this was obtained in some clear and unambiguous experiments by Barton and his co-workers (14). The alcohol (XXXVII) containing the grouping (XXXIII) was treated with phosphorus pentachloride. The same ring contraction as previously described occurred and gave (XXXVIII). Since the chromophore changed from λ_{max}. 285 mμ (in XXXVII) to 265 and 363 mμ (in XXXVIII), the introduced double bond was conjugated with the main chromophoric system. This was confirmed by peroxide fission to (XXXIX) which still contained an extended conjugated system.

It has been suggested that the α positions to the chromophore (XXXIII) are occupied by quaternary carbon atoms; some of these must be methyl groups. The isolation of 1:2:8-trimethylphenanthrene (XXV) by selenium dehydrogenation was open to two interpretations. Either the ring containing two methyl groups was ring

(XXIX)   (XXX)   (XXXI)

(XXIX)   (XXXII)   (XXXIII)   (XXXIV)

(XXXV)   (XXXVI)

(XXXVII)   (XXXVIII)   (XXXIX)

A or it was ring C, as shown in (XL) and (XLI), respectively. In the former case the uncoupling of the methyl groups and migration would be initiated by the adjacent hydroxyl group, as in the case of columbin (page 58). This possibility was eliminated when it was found that the hydrocarbon lanostene (XLII) gave a *greater* yield of the hydrocarbon than did lanosterol. It therefore followed that a methyl group was attached both at C_{13} and C_{14} in lanosterol giving the part formula (XLIII). Ring D was attached in the manner shown, but the size of this ring was as yet unknown.

An indication of the nature of the side-chain was obtained when Barton, McGhie, and their co-workers (16) isolated 6-methylheptan-2-one (XLIV) from the vigorous oxidation of lanostenyl acetate. By the reduction of the diketone (XXX) with sodium and propyl alcohol followed by acetylation, Barton and his co-workers (17) obtained (XLV). This, by vigorous chromic acid oxidation, gave amongst other products, the saturated ketone (XLVI), and the infra-red spectrum of this ketone showed that the carbonyl group was in a five-membered ring. Also, from quantitative measurements in the infra-red (at 1410 cm^{-1}) in the region associated with methylene groups adjacent to carbonyl groups, it was concluded that the carbonyl group was flanked by one, and not two, methylene groups. Position 16 which was in accord with the isoprene rule was therefore excluded for the attachment of the side-chain. The same conclusion as regards the size of ring D was reached by Jeger, Ruzicka, and their colleagues by a stepwise

(XL)

(XLI)

(XLII)

(XLV) $\longrightarrow$ (XLVI)

(XLIII)

(XLIV)

degradation of lanosterol to (XLVIII). The starting material was crude "*iso*cholesterol." This was oxidised with chromic acid in which process three carbon atoms from the side-chain were lost, leaving amongst other products, a C_{27} acid. The enedione chromophore (XXIX) was simultaneously introduced and the alcohol was oxidised to ketone. After Wolff-Kishner reduction and methylation it was possible to isolate the pure ester (XLVII). This was degraded as shown by a modification of the Barbier-Wieland method (19,20). The carbonyl groups remaining in (XLIX) are resistant to Wolff-Kishner reduction under normal conditions.

The possible point of attachment of the side-chain was now limited to C_{15} or C_{17}, C_{16} having been excluded. Of these C_{15} fits the isoprene rule, which C_{17} does not, but on the other hand C_{17} is suggested by analogy with the steroids. The decision in favour of C_{17} was made, chemically (21), by the degradation of the compound

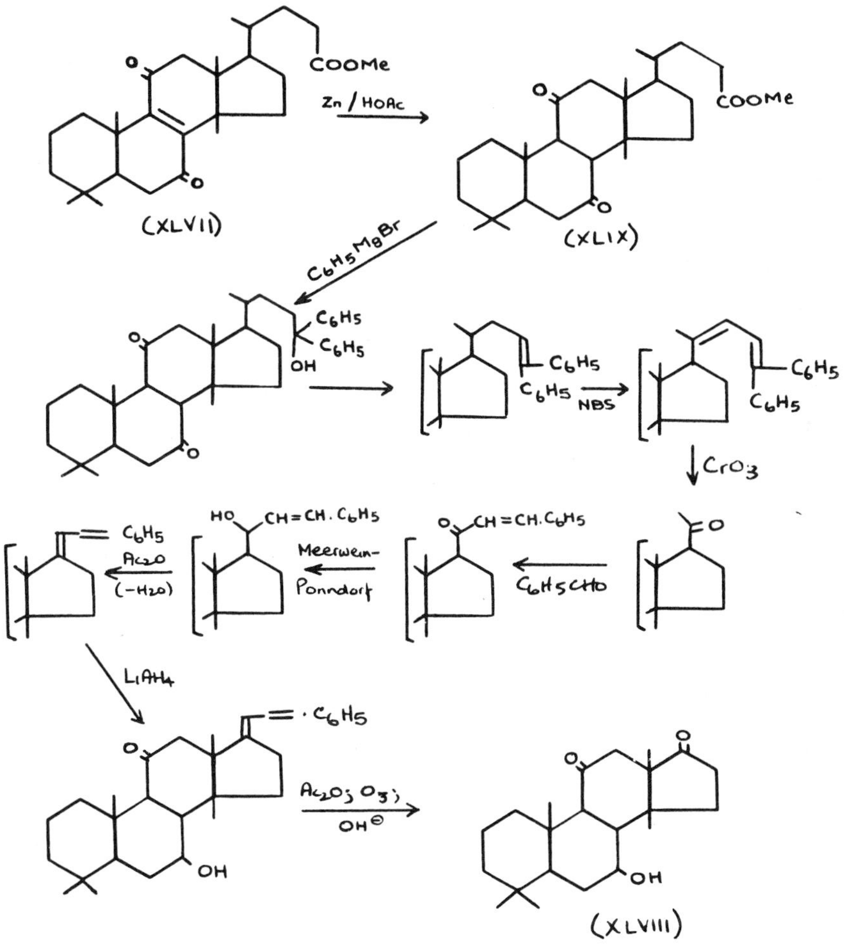
COOMe
Zn / HOAc
(XLVII)
COOMe
(XLIX)
C6H5MgBr
C6H5
C6H5
OH
C6H5
C6H5
NBS
C6H5
C6H5
CrO3
HO
CH=CH.C6H5
O
CH=CH.C6H5
C6H5
Ac2O
(−H2O)
Meerwein-
Ponndorf
C6H5CHO
LiAlH4
·C6H5
Ac2O; O3;
OH⊖
OH
OH
(XLVIII)

(L). This was obtained in a manner similar to (XLIX); the carbonyl group at C_7, being more reactive than that at C_{11}, was removed by formation of the ethylene thioketal $R \cdot C = (SCH_2 \cdot CH_2S)$ and desulphurisation with Raney nickel. Stepwise degradation gave, by steps similar to those already shown, (LI), which was then oxidised successively by a variety of reagents to give, through an intermediate β-keto acid, (LIII). Since during the formation of (LIII) the carboxyl in (LIV) had been lost, and since the equivalent compound (LII) prepared in a similar way was stable, it follows that the driving force for decarboxylation to (LIII) must be the newly introduced carbonyl group. It must therefore be β to the carboxyl, that is at C_{17}.

Shortly prior to this last series of experiments, and before the position of attachment of the side-chain was known, the complete structure, as revealed by X-ray diffraction analysis of lanostenyl iodoacetate, was announced. This, of course, included the stereochemical details (22) shown in (XXI). Chemical evidence was also forthcoming, and molecular rotation arguments further suggested that the stereochemistry paralleled that of the steroids, the representation of which is the absolute configuration. A degradation

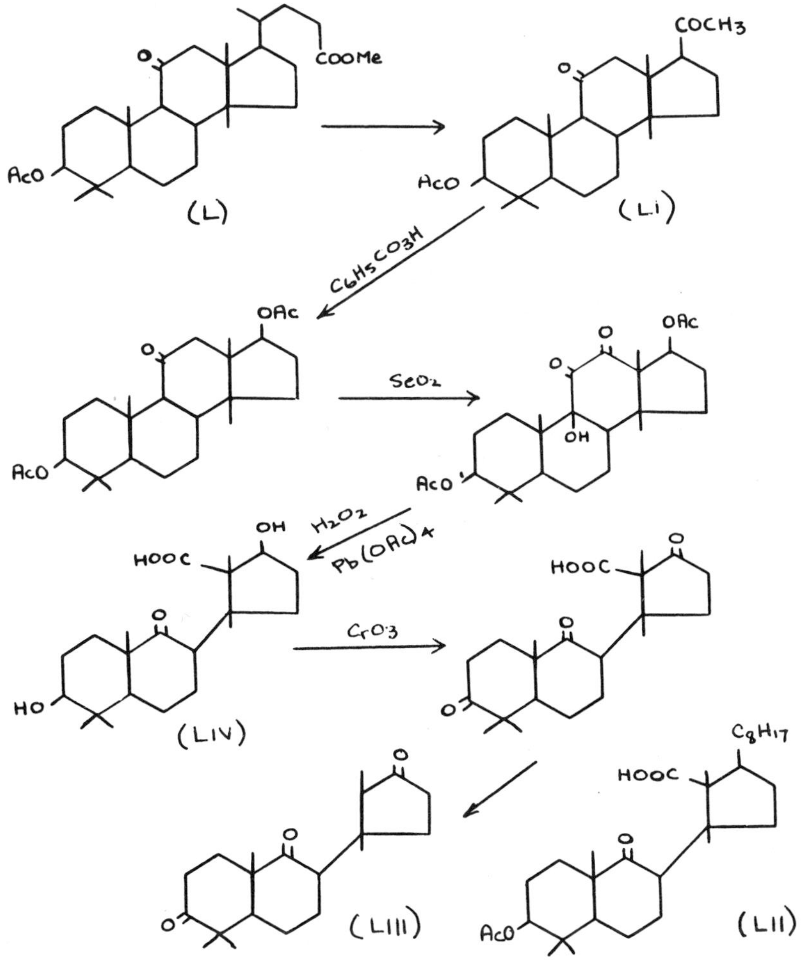
COOMe
COCH3
AcO
(L)
AcO
(Li)
C6H5CO3H
OAc
O
AcO
SeO2
O
OAc
OH
AcO
OH
H2O2
Pb(OAc)4
HOOC
HO
(LIV)
CrO3
HOOC
O
C8H17
HOOC
(LIII)
AcO
(LII)

product (LVI) of some interest was obtained from (LV). This acid had previously been obtained from manool, and manool in turn has been correlated with abietic acid and with oleanolic acid. The isolation of (LVI) therefore amounted to a correlation, in terms of absolute configuration, of lanosterol with the diterpenoids and the pentacyclic triterpenoids.

One further transformation product of lanosteryl acetate requires mention. With hydrogen chloride in chloroform it is partly converted into *iso*lanosteryl acetate (LVII), a mixture of this and lanosteryl acetate being obtained from whichever side the equilibrium is reached. The ethylenic linkage resists hydrogenation, as does that in lanosterol. Proof of its position was obtained, amongst other ways, when it was found that it was produced from the ketone (LVIII) by Wolff-Kishner reduction. In this reaction a bond migration takes place and is a well-established process. Presumably the carbanion obtained in the Wolff-Kishner decomposition prefers to protonate after, and not before, an allylic rearrangement; alternatively the loss of nitrogen may take place through a six-membered cyclic transition state.

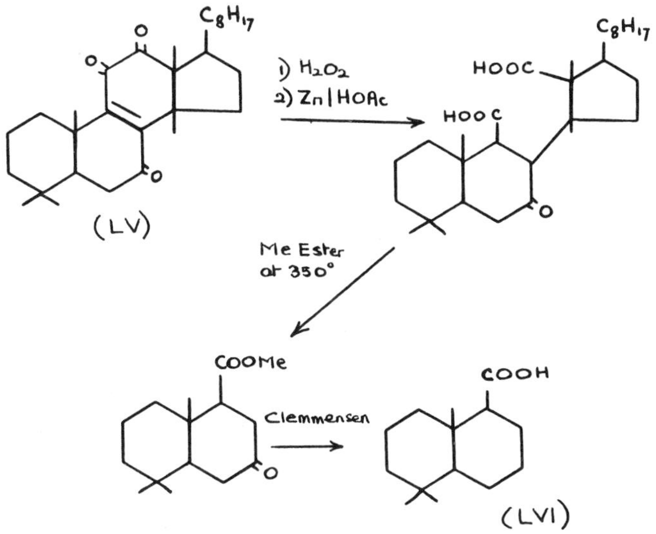

C_8H_{17}
O
O
O
(LV)
1) H_2O_2
2) Zn | HOAc
HOOC
HOOC
C_8H_{17}
O
Me Ester
at 350°
COOMe
O
Clemmensen
COOH
(LVI)

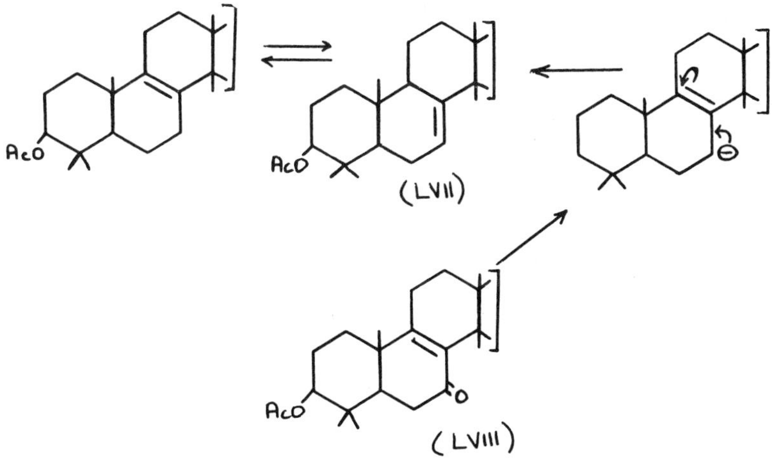

AcO
AcO
(LVII)
AcO
O
(LVIII)

Shortly after the constitution of lanosterol was established the conversion of cholesterol (LIX) into lanostenol was reported. Some time later, the further conversion of lanostenol to both lanosterol and agnosterol having been accomplished, this completed the total synthesis of all the wool fat triterpenoids. The synthetic route is summarised (23) in the scheme opposite. Although the original paper must be consulted for details of the processes involved, some few aspects of this brilliant synthesis will be considered here. The methylation of (LX) to (LXI) appears to be a fairly general phenomenon, and examples of this reaction on simpler substances were recorded by Conia (24). The rearrangement of the diene (LXII) to (LXIII) is one encountered in steroid chemistry in the formation of ergosterol-B III. Introduction of the methyl group at C_{14} must occur from the rear of the molecule because of the considerable steric hindrance to the frontal approach of a reagent. The oxidation of (LXIV) (lanostenyl acetate) to (LXV) with the loss of three carbon atoms occurs under vigorous oxidative conditions and in somewhat poor yield. The same compound was obtained also from the lanosterol mixture from isocholesterol and was used as a relay. The Huang-Minlon modified Wolff-Kishner reduction was sufficient to remove the C_7 carbonyl group; the more forcing conditions necessary to remove the C_{11} carbonyl group could not be used directly on the enedione (LXV) since the intermediate double bond was then reduced, possibly by the alkoxide. This could be used, however, after the C_7 carbonyl group had been removed. The intermediate (LXVII) was reduced with lithium alumi-

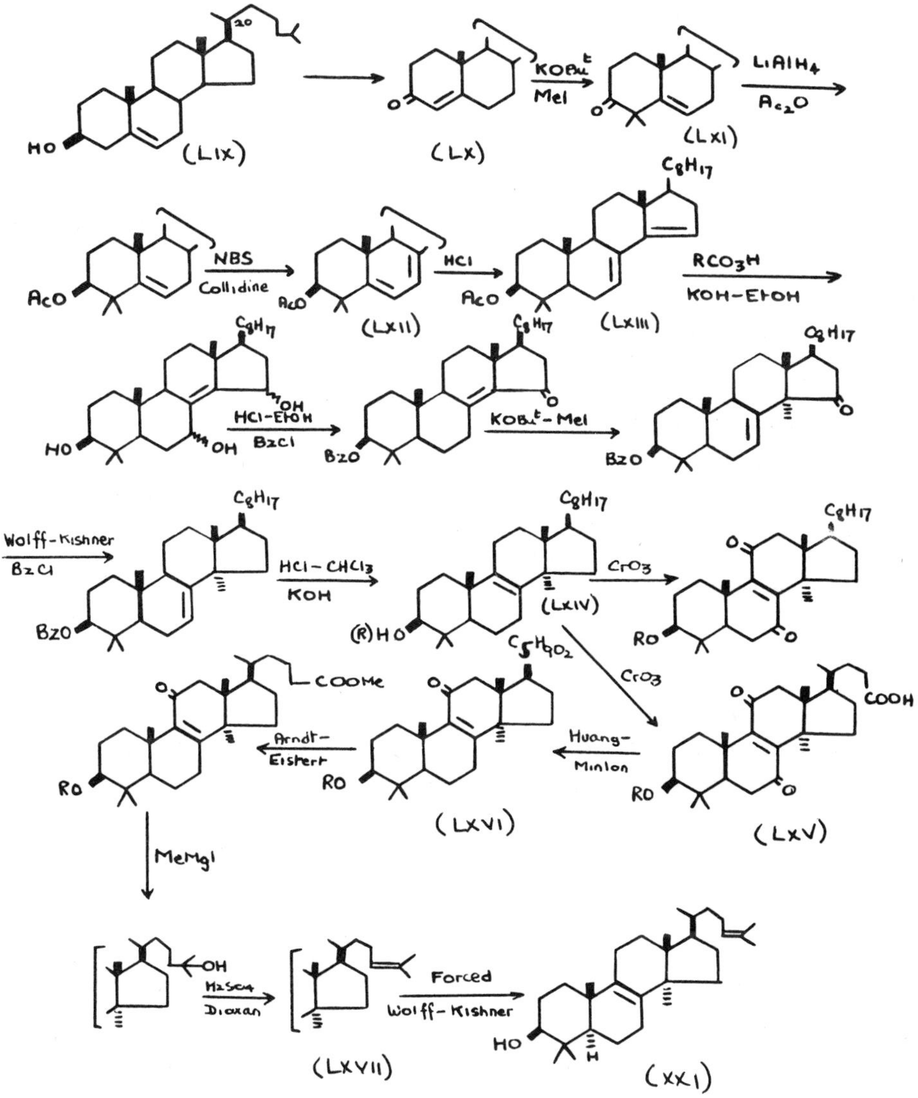
HO
(LIX)
(LX)
KOBu^t
MeI
(LXI)
LiAlH$_4$
Ac$_2$O
AcO
NBS
Collidine
(LXII)
HCl
C_8H_{17}
(LXIII)
RCO$_3$H
KOH-EtOH
HCl-EtOH
BzCl
BzO
KOBu^t-MeI
Wolff-Kishner
BzCl
HCl-CHCl$_3$
KOH
(R)HO
(LXIV)
CrO$_3$
RO
$C_5H_{10}O_2$
COOMe
COOH
Arndt-Eistert
Huang-Minlon
(LXVI)
(LXV)
MeMgI
OH
H$_2$SO$_4$
Dioxan
(LXVII)
Forced
Wolff-Kishner
H
(XXI)

nium hydride to the allylic alcohol (LXVIII). This, on heating with acetic anhydride and a trace of toluene-*p*-sulphonic acid, gave agnosteryl acetate. By inter-relating lanosterol with other triterpenoids, the deduction of these structures was, in turn, now possible.

Cycloartenol

One of these, *cyclo*artenol (LXIX), was the first triterpenoid to be discovered containing a *cyclo*propane ring (25). The presence of this unusual function was shown spectroscopically and, more persuasively, by cleavage with acid to form a double bond. Later, Spring and his associates (26) showed that the main product of the cleavage was lanost-9(11)-enyl acetate (LXX). This had been prepared from the ketone (LXXI) by reduction and dehydration. The problem remaining was the decision between a number of possibilities for the position of the *cyclo*propane ring. The position was simplified when it was shown by Cole (27) that *cyclo*artenol had a band in the infra-red at 3045 cm^{-1} characteristic of a methylene group in a *cyclo*propane ring. On the assumption that the ion (LXXII) is the product of *cyclo*propane cleavage, and that rearrangement does not occur, only two structures are possible for *cyclo*artanol. The reason for the postulation of the ion (LXXII) was that the 9(11) double bond could not be isomerised under the acid conditions used for ring opening nor could the 8:9 and 7:8 double bonds be isomerised to it. Of the two structures, (LXXIII) and (LXXV), the former, which would require non-Markownikoff cleavage of the *cyclo*propane ring, was excluded by Spring and his colleagues (26) by ring opening with deuterium chloride, a technique first used on phyllanthol (page 168). If (LXXIII) had been correct, oxidation to (LXXIV) would have removed the deuterium; (LXXIV) still contained the original deuterium content. The correctness of (LXXV), the alternative, was shown by Spring and his co-workers by conversion of *cyclo*artanone (LXXVI) to the $\alpha : \beta$-unsaturated ketone (LXXVII) which showed in its ultraviolet spectrum that the double bond was conjugated with the *cyclo*propane ring. The same conclusion was reached by Barton, Warn-

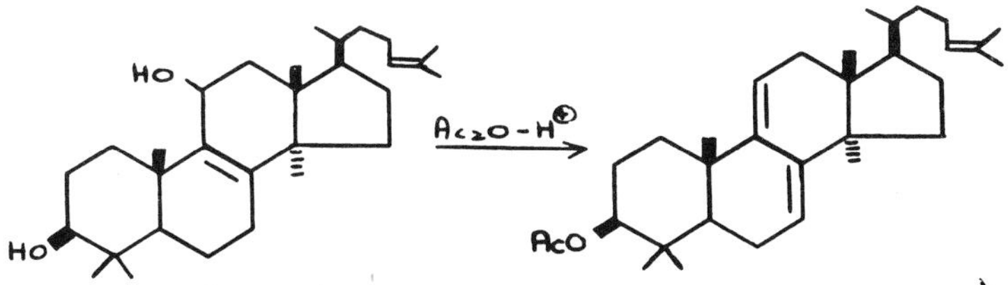

(LXVIII) $Ac_2O-H^{\oplus}$ (XXIII-acetate)

(LXIX)   (LXX)

(LXXII)   (LXXI)

(LXXV)   (LXXIII)   (LXXIV)

(LXXVI)   NBS / Collidine   (LXXVII)

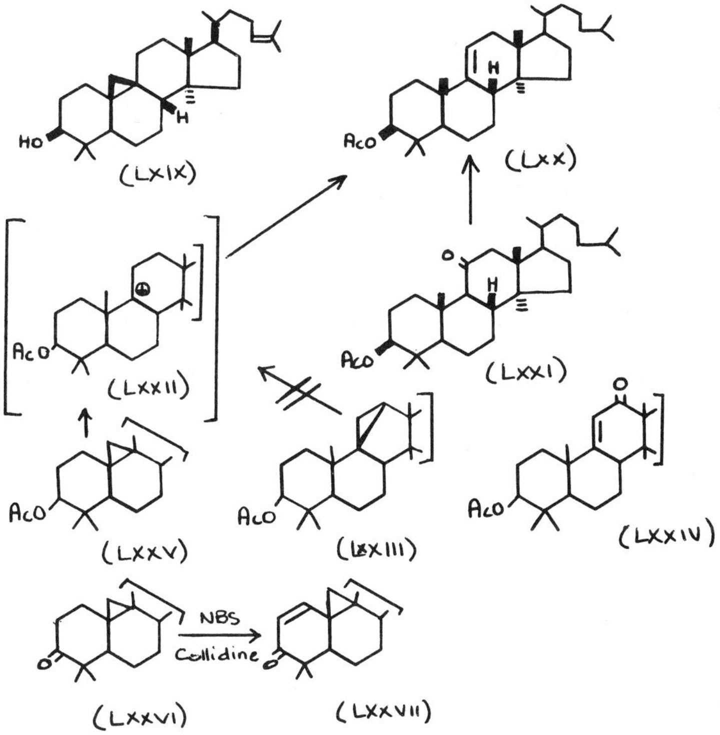

hoff, and Page (28) who carried out quantitative measurements on the 1380 cm^{-1} band in the infra-red on the deuterated (LXXVIII) and non-deuterated lanost-9(11)-ene. This band (CH bending) is characteristic of non-geminal methyl groups. The grouping — CH$_2$D does not absorb in this place, and these authors were able to show that the deuteration resulted in a diminished intensity in this region. It is interesting that the cleavage of the *cyclo*propane ring is diaxial in the manner analogous to that of epoxides. The solution of this structural problem presents an elegant employment of modern techniques. It will be noted that the presence of the *cyclo*propane ring together with the known configuration at C$_8$ (β) in (LXX) requires that the ring B/C fusion in (LXIX) be *cis*.

Shortly after the problem of *cyclo*artenol was solved a related compound having, however, thirty-one carbon atoms was isolated from opium. This substance, **cyclolaudenol (LXXIX) (29)**, was degarded to the methyl ketone (LXXX) also obtained from *cyclo*artenol. The carbon skeleton of *cyclo*laudenol is the same as that of a number of triterpenoids isolated from wood-rotting fungi (Basidiomycetes). These triterpenoids are acids and are obtained from naturally grown fungi and also from fungi grown on a medium in which glucose is the sole source of carbon. They appear to be accompanied by related substances, as in the case of agnosterol with lanosterol, with a heteroannular diene spectrum. A number of these are illustrated opposite. They are **eburicoic acid (LXXXI), dehydroeburicoic acid (LXXXII), polyporenic acid A, (LXXXIII), tumulosic**

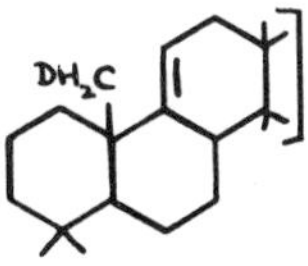
DH₂C

(LXXVIII)

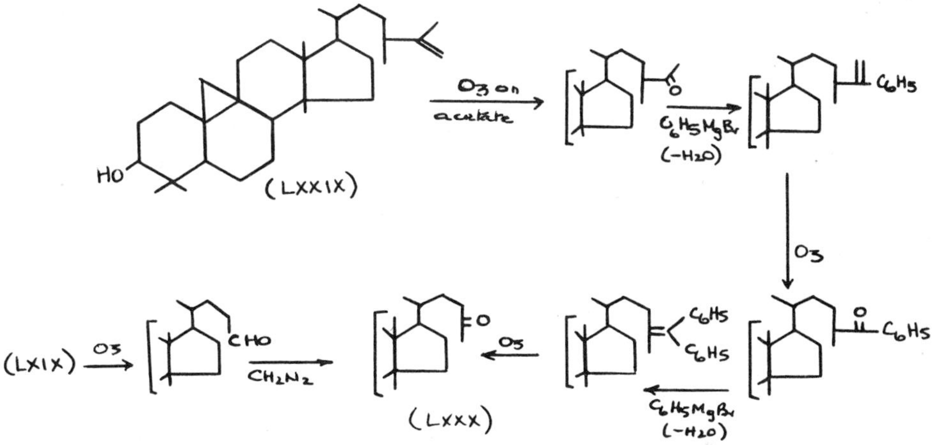
HO
(LXXIX)
O₃ on
acetate
C₆H₅MgBr
(−H₂O)
C₆H₅
O₃
C₆H₅
C₆H₅
C₆H₅
C₆H₅MgBr
(−H₂O)
O₃
(LXXX)
CH₂N₂
CHO
(LXIX)
O₃

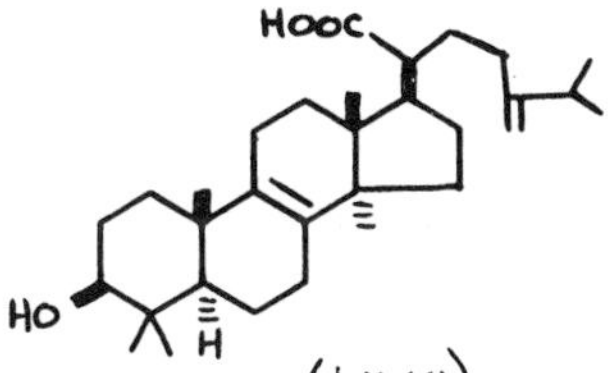
HOOC
HO
H

(LXXXI)

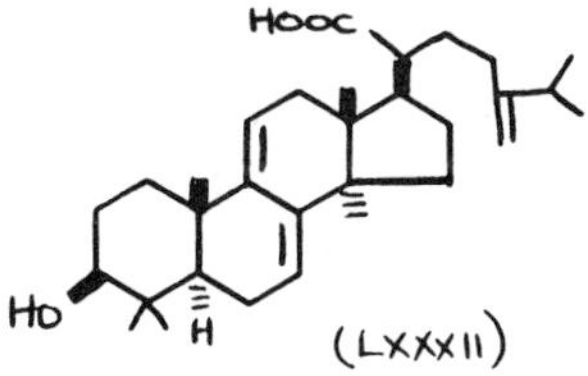
HOOC
HO
H

(LXXXII)

acid (LXXXIV), **polyporenic acid C** (LXXXV), and the C_{30} compound **pinicolic acid A** (LXXXVI) (30).

Euphol

The parent substance of the second main group of tetracyclic triterpenoids, euphol (LXXXVII), was first isolated in a pure condition by Newbold and Spring from euphorbium resin and it has since been isolated from a number of *Euphorbia* species. These authors showed that euphol was a tetracyclic alcohol, $C_{30}H_{50}O$, and that it had two double bonds, one of which could be hydrogenated. This reducible double bond was shown to be part of an *iso*propylidene group. On selenium dehydrogenation $1:2:8$-trimethylphenanthrene was the only product. These reactions parallel those of lanosterol very closely. The similarity was emphasised when the diketone (LXXXVIII) was obtained from dihydroeuphyl acetate (euphenyl acetate) (LXXXIX) by chromic acid oxidation. Further evidence was obtained when it was shown that euphol underwent the typical triterpenoid alcohol ring A contractions. Also, oxidation of (LXXXVIII) with selenium dioxide led to the same diene-trione chromophore (XXXIII) as had been obtained from lanosterol indicative of the same partial structure (XLIII).

These resemblances were immediately striking. Evidences for differences, though of a more subtle kind, also began to accumulate. The oxides, for instance, of the inert double bond in lanosterol derivatives are very unstable giving the heteroannular dienes very easily. The corresponding euphol derivatives require acidic dehydrating agents for this reaction. There were also small differences in the position of the chromophores in the ultra-violet, and larger discrepancies in molecular rotation differences.

The most important difference in behaviour was the transformation of euphenyl acetate to *iso*euphenyl acetate with acid. This reaction is not the same change as the conversion of lanostenyl acetate to *iso*lanostenyl acetate, that is merely the shift of a double bond. Both spectral and chemical evidence indicated that the double bond in *iso*euphenyl acetate was tetrasubstituted. Thus reaction with osmium tetroxide (31) gave a glycol cleaved with lead tetraacetate to a diketone; this diketone did not react with hypo-

(LXXXIII)

(LXXXVI)

(LXXXV)

(LXXXIV)

(LXXXVII)

(LXXXIX)

(LXXXVIII)

iodite. It was believed, also, that ring D was five-membered as in the lanosterol series because the intensity of the 1380 cm^{-1} band of euphene and lanostene were identical, requiring the same number of methyl groups, leaving, therefore, no unaccounted for carbon atoms. Nevertheless, the reason for the different course of the acid-catalysed reaction was attributed to some feature in ring D.

It was first considered that the rearrangement might proceed in a manner somewhat similar to the behaviour of certain Λ^8 steroids though the latter have, of course, the side-chain attached to C_{17}. In that case the change of euphenyl acetate to *iso*euphenyl acetate would be represented by the partial formulae (XC) and (XCI). But the formulation (XC) for euphenyl acetate did not account for the formation of 1 : 2 : 8-trimethylphenanthrene on dehydrogenation. This required the presence of methyl groups at both C_{13} and C_{14} and led to the proposal that the change might be represented as (XCII) → (XCIII). This structure for *iso*euphenyl acetate was later rendered untenable (32) when it was shown that the diketone obtained by cleavage of the double bond reacted with five moles of bromine. This diketone on the basis of (XCIII), would be (XCIV) having 3 α hydrogens only. To account for this and for the spectroscopic evidence for two —— CH_2—— CO —— groups it was proposed that *iso*euphenyl acetate was (XCV) and the diketone (XCVI). The same conclusion was reached by a more systematic degradation. Oxidation (33) of *iso*euphenyl acetate with *tert*-butyl chromate gave amongst other products the $\alpha : \beta$-unsaturated ketone (XCVII). Ozonolysis led to cleavage of the double bond and the formation of a

(XC)

(XCI)

(XCII)

(XCIII)

(XCIV)

(XCV)

(XCVI)

C_8H_{17}

(XCVII)

C_{21} keto acid (XCVIII) and optically pure D(−)-2 : 6-dimethylheptanoic acid (XCIX). These facts require that the five angular methyl groups in isoeuphenol be in rings A, B, and C. Dehydrogenation of euphadiene (C) gave, as expected, 1 : 2 : 8-trimethylphenanthrene; isoeuphadiene (CI) gave 1 : 2 : 5-trimethylnaphthalene. The fission of the molecule between rings B and C, because of the presence of the angular methyl group at C_8, occurs also in the pentacyclic triterpenoids. Aromaticity can only be achieved by elimination of this group or by fission. The formulation of a structure for euphol requires that the evidence for ring D, the dehydrogenation products, and the conversion to isoeuphol type substances be accommodated. It is also required to explain why a similar rearrangement does not take place in the lanosterol series. This is explained by the structure (LXXXVII). If the first step in the rearrangement of both lanosterol and euphol derivatives is protonation at C_9 then the ions (CII) and (CIII) result. In (CII) the methyl at C_{14}, should it move, will do so over the α face of the molecule to give the ion (CIV) in which there is now an unfavourable cis B/C fusion. The elimination of a proton from C_7 is therefore preferred. In (CIII) movement of the C_{14} methyl over the β face will give (CV). Here there is a trans B/C fusion which is far less strained than that in (CIV). Conversion to isoeuphenyl derivatives then takes place by migration of the methyl group at C_{13} and elimination of a proton from C_{17}. It is possible that this remarkable series of migrations is concerted. If so then the side-chain would be required to have the α configuration to permit the concerted elimination of the C_{17} proton, and this has in fact been established.*

The difference between euphol and lanosterol may be summarised as follows. In euphol, rings B and C are in an unfavourable conformation, and in forming isoeuphol the molecule is permitted to assume the favourable all-chair conformation (with a trans- anti-trans junction). In lanosterol there is no such conversion to a

---

*If the reaction is concerted it should be noted that, in the case of lanosterol, protonation would be required to take place from the very hindered β face.

(XC VIII)

(XCIX)

(C)

(CI)

(CII)   (CIII)   (CIV)   (CV)

favourable conformation possible since it is (again allowing for the double bonds) already in the favoured all-chair conformation. Since in the conversion of euphol to *iso*euphol a preferred conformation is adopted this has been considered to be the driving force for the reaction. The term "conformational driving force" has been proposed (32).

Tirucallol

The configuration at C_{20} in euphol, as shown by the isolation of D(–)-2 : 6-dimethylheptanoic acid, is the same as in the steroids. The triterpenoid tirucallol was first isolated by Haines and Warren from *Euphorbia tirucalli* resin (34) in which euphol and the pentacyclic triterpenoid taraxasterol also occur. In its transformations it closely parallels euphol with which it is isomeric. By a degradation identical with that performed on euphol, tirucallol gave L(+)-2 : 6-dimethylheptanoic acid, that is the enantiomorph of that obtained from euphol (35). Tirucallol was therefore presumed to differ from euphol only in the configuration at C_{20} and may be represented by (CVI). This was later confirmed by the production from elemolic acid of both euphol and tirucallol by steps not involving C_{17}. **Euphorbol** (CVII), also isolated from *Euphorbia* species, is a C_{31} compound (36). By ozonolysis and Wolff-Kishner reduction euphorbol yielded tirucallenol. This established all but the position of the extra carbon atom lost as formaldehyde during the ozonolysis; analogy suggested that this was at C_{24}, and this was later confirmed. Manila elemi resin contains in the acid fraction two substances, α-elemolic acid and the corresponding keto acid, β-elemonic acid. The prefixes, arising out of some confusion in the literature, need not be further used. Most of the chemistry of these substances again paralleled that of tirucallol. The alcohol had in this case, however, the α configuration (axial hydroxyl), the epimer being prepared by the reduction of elemonic acid. Although the elemi acids were extensively investigated—they were the first tetracyclic triterpenoids to be studied in detail—the elucidation of their structure awaited that of tirucallol. By the stages shown, elemonic acid (CVIII) was converted into tirucallenol. A by-product

(CVI)

(CVII)

(CVIII) $H_2 \longrightarrow$

Ac_2O
$SOCl_2$

Rosenmund

Wolff-
Kishner

(38) obtained in the reduction of the aldehyde was euphenol. This established conclusively, since this reaction did not involve C_{17}, that tirucallol and euphol differ only at C_{20}.

This series of reactions whilst establishing much of the structure and stereochemistry of the elemi acids did not fix the position of the carboxyl group. Although at one time considered tertiary because of its degree of hindrance, further work—for instance, the isolation of the C_{20} isomer euphenol—already mentioned, showed that it was in fact secondary, and its position with respect to the side-chain was clearly demonstrated by the cyclisation of acetyl-elemolic acid (CIX) with phosphorus pentoxide to an $\alpha : \beta$-unsaturated ketone (CIXA) (35,37).

These investigations into the relative stereochemistry of the lanosterol–euphol–euphorbol–elemolic acid group reached a brilliant culmination in some work of the Zurich school (38). It had previously been shown by Barton and his colleagues that the di-

(CIX)

(CIX a)

carboxylic acid (CXXXIV) obtained from lanosterol, when heated, lost carbon dioxide to give a neutral product—the phenolic lactone (CX). This was probably formed by the steps shown. During this transformation the asymmetry at C_8 and C_{10} is destroyed. By a similar series of transformations on tirucall-8-en-3 α-ol (CXI) the Zurich school obtained the lactone (CXII) which was the enantiomorph of (CX). This elegant work showed that the compounds of the elemolic acid–euphorbol–tirucallol series differed from lanosterol at C_{13}, C_{14}, C_{17}, and C_{20}, whilst euphol differed at C_{13}, C_{14}, and C_{17} only. Further confirmation of the diastereoisomerism of euphol and tirucallol has been provided by Warren and Watling who have transformed tirucalla-8:24-diene and the analogous euphadiene by degradation of the side-chain into products containing the side-chain $—CMe = CH \cdot CH = C(C_6H_5)_2$ in which the asymmetry of C_{20} has been eliminated. The identity of the two products shows that the stereochemistry at C_{20} was the only difference (39).

Butyrospermol

Butyrospermol, isolated from shea nut fat, was first characterised in pure form by Heilbron, Jones, and Robins in 1949. Like so many other members of this group it is a secondary alcohol with one easily reduced double bond present in an *iso*propylidene group and a second double bond resistant to hydrogenation. Addition of bromine to the side-chain double bond in butyrospermyl acetate, treatment with hydrogen chloride at $0°$, and regeneration of the side-chain ethylenic linkage with zinc gave euphyl acetate. In a similar way dihydrobutyrospermyl acetate gave euphenyl acetate. Complications were at first encountered because of reaction of the hydrogen chloride with the side-chain double bond. *Iso*butyrospermyl acetate obtained in this way was later shown to be eupha-

(CXXXIV)

(CX)

(CXI) $\xrightarrow{\text{several steps}}$ (CXII)

8:25-dienyl acetate (CXIII).   The conditions of acidity required
to convert dihydrobutyrospermol to euphenol were milder than those
required to isomerise euphenol to *iso*euphenol.   Since dihydrobutyrospermol underwent the usual ring contraction and the product
is not a conjugated diene, a possible structure (CXIV), which would
have involved rearrangement in the formation of euphenol, was excluded (40).   It followed that butyrospermol was represented by the
part formulae (CXV) or (CXVI).   This view was reached also by
Spring and his collaborators (41).   The precise location of the
double bond was ascertained independently by both groups. Halsall,
Jones, and their co-workers (40) isomerised dihydrobutyrospermyl acetate in chloroform with deuterium chloride.   The product should
have been (CXVII) or (CXVIII) depending on whether (CXV) or
(CXVI) were correct. Oxidation with chromic acid gave the 7-ketone
(CXIX), which was shown to contain no deuterium.   After demonstrating that (CXIX) was not formed through the diene (CXX), this
transformation proved the correctness of the formulation (CXV).   By
the oxidation of dihydrobutyrospermyl acetate with chromic acid
Spring and his co-workers (41) isolated a ketone which contained
an isolated ehtylenic linkage (yellow colour with tetranitromethane).
This compound, oxo*apo*euphenyl acetate was stable to chromic acid
and was unaffected by treatment with acid or base.   Under vigorous
acid conditions (hydrochloric–acetic acid) an isomeric non-conjugated ketone was obtained, reduction of which by the forcing
modification of the Wolff-Kishner reactions (42) gave *iso*euphenyl
acetate.   The isomeric ketone with the *iso*euphenol skeleton did
not have this oxygen function at C_{11} or C_{12} because oxidation of
this ketone with selenium dioxide gave a keto *iso*eupha-11:13(17)-
dienyl acetate having the same spectrum in the ultra-violet as

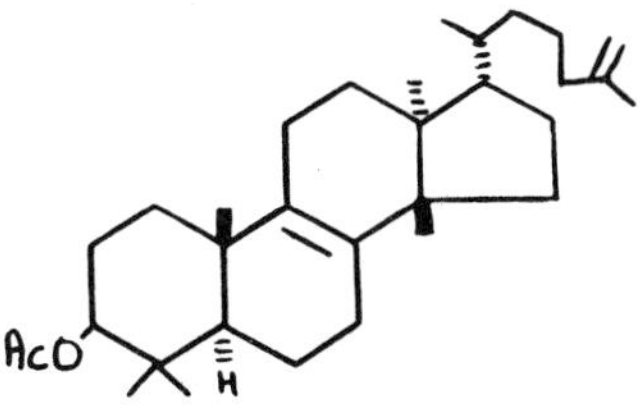

(CXIII)

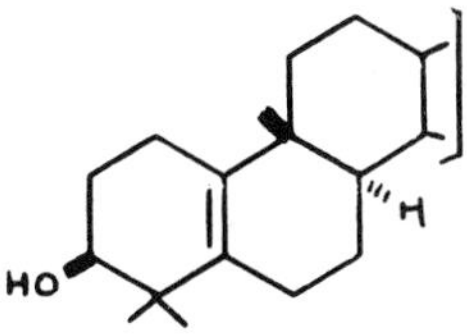

(CXIV)

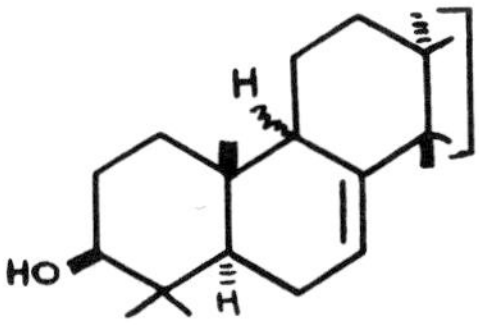

(CXV)

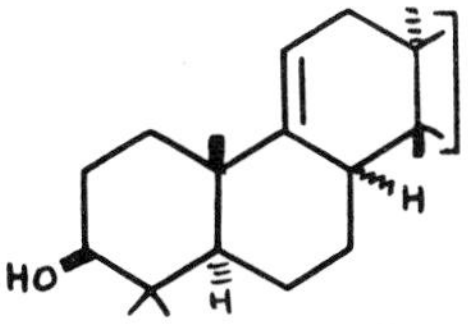

(CXVI)

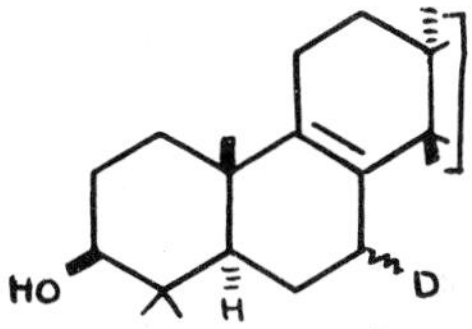

(CXVII)

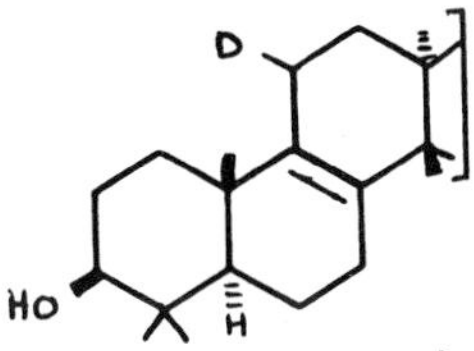

(CXVIII)

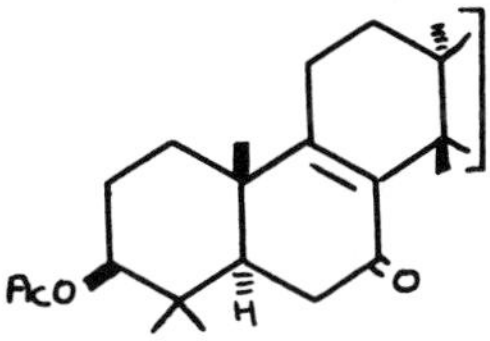

(CXIX)

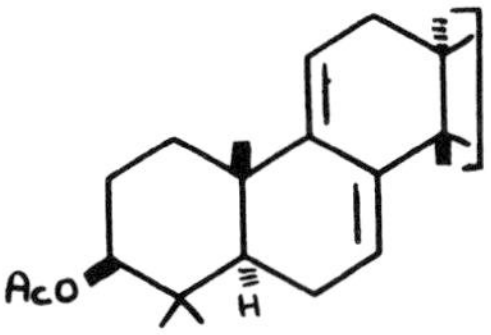

(CXX)

(CXXI). The latter is obtained from *iso*euphenyl acetate by the same reagent. It followed that the carbonyl group was at C_6 or C_7. Two possible structures (CXXII) and (CXXIII) for oxo*apo*euphenyl acetate were excluded because they should be isomerisable to α: β-unsaturated ketones. Also, in the case of (CXXII), the formation of oxo*apo*euphenyl acetate can only be visualised as proceeding through a diene such as (CXX); this was shown not to be an intermediate. (CXXIII) was also rejected because, apart from other reasons, the infra-red spectrum indicated that the isolated double bond was trisubstituted. The elimination of (CXXII) and (CXXIII) requires that some rearrangement take place during the oxidation. That there was a rearrangement was confirmed by the fact that *apo*euphenyl acetate (obtained from the ketone by Wolff-Kishner reduction and reacetylation) on mild acid treatment gave *iso*euphenyl acetate, whereas, in contrast, under the same conditions euphenyl acetate was unchanged and dihydrobutyrospermyl acetate was converted only to euphenyl acetate. It was then suggested that this rearrangement to the *apo* series was initiated by the oxidation at the 7:8 double bond with a synchronous migration of the C_{14} methyl group to C_8. The ion (CXXIV) could then proceed to give either (CXXV) or (CXXVI). Both (CXXV) and (CXXVI) may be conceived as giving rise, after protonation, to the *iso*euphenyl system. Although not rigidly proven Spring and his co-workers prefer (CXXV) and have provided evidence to support their view. However, in either case the ketone must be at C_7, and this was confirmed by oxidation with selenium dioxide of the *apo*ketone to the α:β-unsaturated ketone (CXXVII) which rearranged with acid to give the *iso*euphenyl skeleton. Since the postulated rearrangement does not involve C_9, the configuration here must be the same as in *iso*-euphenol. Butyrospermol is thus (CXXVIII). The mildness of the conditions under which the rearrangement takes place is presumably another example of a conformational driving force.

Masticadienonic Acid

Gum mastic has been known and used for a very long period as a varnish. Although examined previously by Tschirch and Reutter

(CXXI)   (CXXII)   (CXXIII)

(CXIV)

(CXXVI)   (CXXV)

(CXXVII)   (CXXVIII)

and by Casparis and Naef, it was not known to contain triterpenoids until examined by Mills by a paper chromatographic technique (43). This analytical method suggested the presence of a number of triterpenoid-like bodies and, following this, the gum was systematically examined by Barton and Seoane (44). Amongst other triterpenoid products a substance, masticadienonic acid, $C_{30}H_{46}O_3$ was obtained. It was an $\alpha:\beta$-unsaturated acid and contained a carbonyl group. The conjugated ethylenic linkage was readily hydrogenated giving the dihydro compound, and this product still contained an isolated double bond. Oxidation of this (CXXIX) with selenium dioxide gave the heteroannular diene (CXXX), and the same chromophore was produced by acid treatment of an epoxide formed from the inert double bond. Attempted hydrogenation in acetic acid with platinum as catalyst gave an isomer (CXXXI) which on oxidation with chromic acid gave the yellow *trans*oid enedione (CXXXII). The nature of the chromophore was confirmed by the ultra-violet spectrum ($\lambda_{max.}$ 270 mμ) and its reduction to the saturated diketone (CXXXIII). The nuclear double bond was therefore at 7:8 (as in CXXIX) or at 9:11.

(CXXIX) $\xrightarrow{SeO_2}$ (CXXX)   (CXXXI)

O_3 $H^{\oplus}$ CrO_3

Zn-HoHc

(CXXXIII)   (CXXXII)

The problem at this stage was the identification of the basic carbon skeleton. Masticadienonic acid (CXXXIV) was converted to the dihydro derivative (CXXXV). This was reduced with lithium aluminium hydride, and the diol converted to the tosylate. Reduction again with lithium aluminium hydride gave (CXXXVI). Acetylation and the process of "hydrogenation" again isomerised the double bond and gave tirucallenol.

Two features remain for clarification. The position of the $\alpha:\beta$-unsaturated carboxyl function was shown by ozonolysis to give acetic acid. The stability to alkali suggested the more stable *trans* configuration (as in tiglic acid) and this was supported by a study of spectra. The choice between the 7:8 and 9:11 position of the double bond was resolved by catalytic deuteration over platinum. The product with the tirucallenyl structure contained the deuterium either at C_7 or C_{11} depending on the position of the original double bond. Ozonisation in ethyl acetate followed by treatment with ferrous ion gave 7-ketotirucallenyl acetate which contained no deuterium. The double bond, as represented in (CXXXIV), was therefore at the 7:8 position; the possibility that the diene (CXXX) was an intermediate in the oxidation, a possibility that would vitiate the results, was experimentally disproved. The configuration at C_9 was not established directly, but molecular rotation evidence strongly suggested that it was α, as in butyrospermol.

Dammaradienol

A number of neutral tetracyclic triterpenoids have been isolated by Mills from dammar resin (45). They consist of dammaradienol and its related ketone, two monoethenoid diols, and their related ketols. These substances were closely related to each other, and the dehydration of both diol monoacetates (in which one hydroxyl group was tertiary) gave mixtures in which the presence of the diethenoid dammaradienyl acetate was shown. These compounds were directly correlated with the tetracyclic triterpenoids already described by hydrogenation of one of the monoethenoid diols monoacetate to the saturated alcohol followed by acid-catalysed dehy-

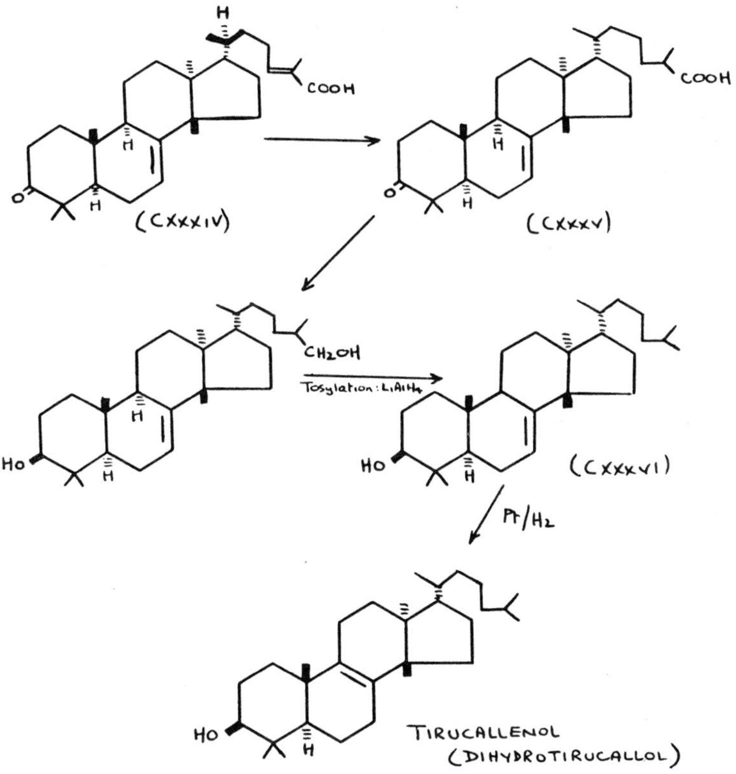

(CXXXIV)

(CXXXV)

CH₂OH

Tosylation : LiAlH₄

(CXXXVI)

Pt/H₂

TIRUCALLENOL
(DIHYDROTIRUCALLOL)

dration. The product was a mixture of *iso*tirucallenyl (CXXXVII) and *iso*euphenyl acetate (CXXXVIII). Their formation must have proceeded through the common ion (CXXXIX). The ion (CXXXIX) could be formed from a number of tertiary alcohols by solvolysis and rearrangement. The position of the hydroxyl group was rigorously demonstrated by dehydration under conditions (phosphorus oxychloride and pyridine) which preclude the possibility of rearrangements through carbonium ions. The product obtained was a mixture of (CXL) and (CXLI), since on subsequent ozonolysis formaldehyde and *iso*hexanal were obtained. Bearing in mind that dammaradienyl acetate is formed by dehydration of the monoethenoid diol monoacetate and that it contains an *exo* methylene group, it follows that it is represented by the part formula (CXLII) with the remaining double bond to be placed.

Oxidation of the monoethenoid ketols with chromic acid under mild conditions resulted in the formation of γ-lactones. Three carbon atoms were lost as acetone. This unusual reaction probably proceeds by the mechanism shown and provides evidence that the ethylenic linkage in these substances is as in lanosterol, tirucallol,

(CXXXIX)

(CXXXVIII)

(CXXXVII)

(CXL)

(CXLI)

(CXLII)

and related compounds. Dammaradienol is therefore (CXLIII) and the diols are represented by (CXLIV).

Although the relationship of this group of substances to euphol and tirucallol is clear, the production of a naturally occurring triterpenoid with the *iso*euphenyl skeleton might be thought surprising. In fact, the occurrence of this type of skeleton was a predictable consequence of a theory of terpenoid biogenesis proposed by Ruzicka. Although this will be dealt with later (Chapter 5), it is sufficient to note here that the theory proposes that all triterpenoids are biogenetically derivable from the acyclic squalene, or its equivalent. During the cyclisation stereospecific rearrangements may take place, all involving $1:2$ shifts, leading to all the known triterpenoid structures in the correct stereochemical forms. At the time of proposal of this theory only squalene itself and ambrein were known which had the squalene skeleton intact. The dammar triterpenoids, discovered later, represented another member of this group. However, their structural elucidation was preceded by that of onocerin, to be described below, which was also a squalene derivative. The cyclisation of squalene to the dammar triterpenoids may be represented as shown opposite.

ONOCERIN

The prediction of this type of structure by the theory represents a considerable triumph. If indeed the process is as described then concertion of the cyclisation process requires that the C_{13} hydrogen be β, a fact not yet verified chemically. The first tetracyclic triterpenoid to be identified as theoretically derivable from squalene by cyclisation without rearrangement was onocerin. It was also the first of these compounds to be found in the vegetable kingdom. Its structure was elucidated by Barton and Overton (46) 100 years after its isolation in 1855 by Hlasiwetz from the restharrow.

Onocerin (α-onoceradienediol) contains two secondary hydroxyl groups and two double bonds both of which are present as *exo* methylene groups. The environment of the hydroxyl groups was suggested to be in the normal 3β position because with phosphorus pentachloride the normal retropinacolic change—dehydration and

(CXLIII)

(CXLIV)

(CXLIV) or (CXLIII)

ring contraction—takes place, ozonolysis then giving the amount of acetone that would suggest *two iso*propylidene groups. The environment of the hydroxyl groups was also suggested by the bromination of the related ketone as shown. These results, together with the isolation of *three* and not *four* saturated α-onoceranediols, suggested the structure (CXLV) which was subsequently elegantly confirmed in every detail.

One remarkable feature of the structure (CXLV) is its symmetry about the X----X axis. This symmetry was shown to exist by the series of reactions opposite. The equivalence of the two hydroxyl groups constitutes a unique feature of the structural determination.

Further evidence as to the carbon skeleton was obtained by dehydrogenation. Selenium dehydrogenation of onocerin itself gave

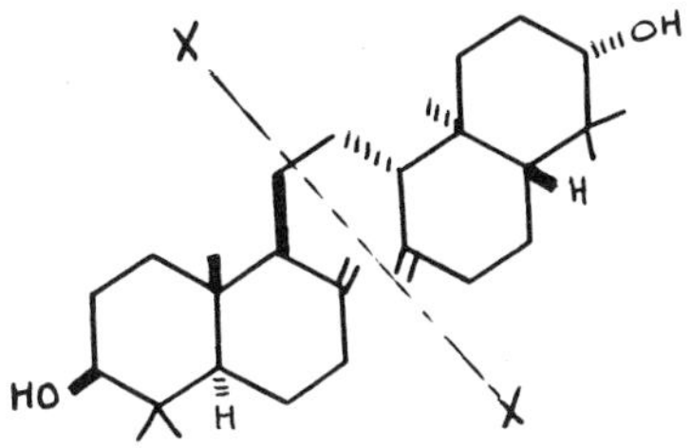

(CXLV)

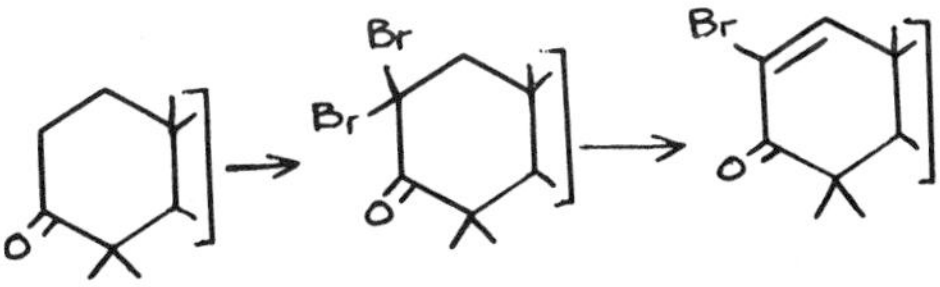

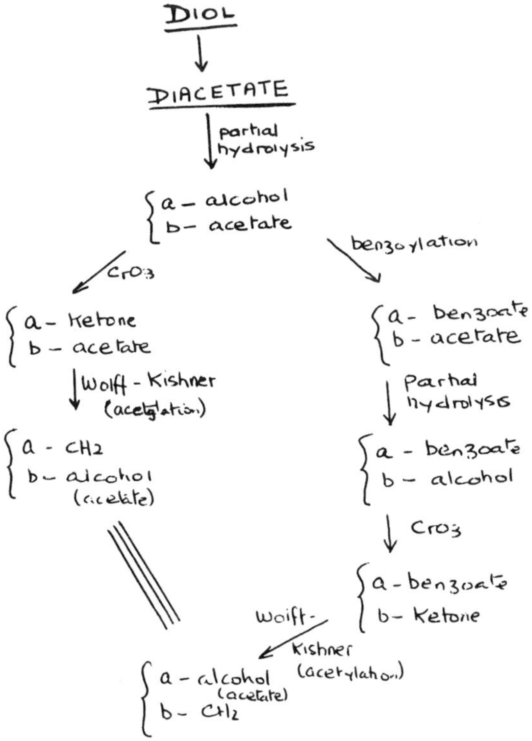

DIOL
↓
DIACETATE
↓ partial
  hydrolysis

{ a – alcohol
{ b – acetate

/ CrO₃   benzoylation ↘

{ a – ketone   { a – benzoate
{ b – acetate   { b – acetate

↓ Wolff – Kishner   ↓ Partial
  (acetylation)   hydrolysis

{ a – CH₂   { a – benzoate
{ b – alcohol   { b – alcohol
   (acetate)
                                          ↓ CrO₃

                                          { a – benzoate
                                          { b – ketone

                    Wolff –
                    kishner (acetylation)
          { a – alcohol (acetate)
          { b – CH₂

(CXLVI) in which, as has been noted before, the elimination of the hydroxyl group next to a geminal dimethyl group points to the migration of one of these methyl groups. Selenium dehydrogenation of the hydrocarbon α-onoceradiene, obtained by oxidation of onocerin to the diketone and Wolff-Kishner reduction, gave (CXLVII) in 68% yield based on *two* molecules of (CXLVII) from one of the hydrocarbon. Finally, the *exo* methylene groups were removed by ozonolysis, and the oxygen functions removed by reduction. Dehydrogenation of this hydrocarbon gave (CXLVIII), proving thereby that the *exo* methylene group was attached at C_8.

By acid treatment of onocerin an isomeric series of compounds based on β-onocerin (β-onoceradienediol) (CXLIX) is obtained. By an elegant degradation of this, Jeger and his co-workers (47) have obtained the dicarboxylic acid (CL) also obtained from dehydroabietic acid (CLI). Since the absolute configuration of abietic acid, and therefore of (CL), is known, that of onocerin follows. Under more vigorous conditions both α and β derivatives are converted into a third series. These γ derivatives contain but one double bond and are therefore pentacyclic. Oxidation of γ-onocerin

(CXLVI)   (CXLVII)   (CXLVIII)

(CXLIX)

(CL)

CCl₃COOH
NaN₃

(CLI)

diacetate (CLII) with chromic acid gave the unsaturated ketone (CLIII). Treatment of the same diacetate with hydrogen peroxide in acetic acid and chloroform gave, presumably by rearrangement of an intermediate epoxide, the ketone (CLIV). This was brominated to (CLV), and on dehydrobromination (CLVI), identical with (CLIII), was obtained. This again proved the symmetry of the molecule and established the location of the single ethylenic linkage. This was also proven by reduction of (CLIII) with lithium aluminium hydride and dehydration with reacetylation to give the homoannular diene (CLVII) ($\lambda_{max.}$ 281 mμ).

The structure of onocerin is interesting both chemically and biogenetically. So far, cyclisations in the laboratory have not succeeded in reproducing the biogenetic process, but it is noteworthy that the cyclisation of squalene has been attempted (48) and the product shown to contain two double bonds. Its structure has not, however, been established.

REFERENCES

1. de Mayo, P., and R. I. Reed, *Chem. & Ind. (London)*, **1956,** 1481.
2. Heilbron, I. M. (Sir), and A. Thompson, *J. Chem. Soc.*, **1929,** 883, and many previous papers.
3. Karrer, P., and A. Helfenstein, *Helv. Chim. Acta*, **14,** 78 (1931).
4. Dauben, W. G., and H. L. Bradlow, *J. Am. Chem. Soc.*, **74,** 5204 (1952).
5. Nicolaides, N., and F. Laves, *J. Am. Chem. Soc.*, **76,** 2596 (1954).
6. Trippett, S., *Chem. & Ind. (London)*, **1956,** 80.
7. Dicker, D. W., and M. C. Whiting, *Chem. & Ind. (London)*, **1956,** 351.
8. Wittig, G., and U. Schollkopf, *Ber.*, **87,** 1318 (1954).
9. Schlessler, R. W., and D. Flitter, *J. Am. Chem. Soc.*, **74,** 1720 (1952).
10. Ruzicka, L., and F. Lardon, *Helv. Chim. Acta*, **29,** 913 (1946).
11. Lederer, E., F. Marx, D. Mercier, and G. Perot, *Helv. Chim. Acta*, **29,** 1354 (1946); Lederer, E., D. Mercier, and G. Perot, *Bull. soc. chim. France*, **1947,** 345.
12. Dietrich, P., and E. Lederer, *Compt. rend.*, **234,** 637 (1952); *Helv. Chim. Acta*, **35,** 1548 (1952).
13. Ruzicka, L., E. Rey, and A. C. Muhr, *Helv. Chim. Acta*, **27,** 472 (1944).
14. Barton, D. H. R., J. S. Fawcett, and B. R. Thomas, *J. Chem. Soc.*, **1951,** 3147; Voser, W., M. Montavan, H. H. Gunthard, O. Jeger, and L. Ruzicka, *Helv. Chim. Acta*, **33,** 1893 (1950).

15. Cavalla, J. F., and J. F. McGhie, *J. Chem. Soc.*, **1951**, 744.
16. Barnes, C. S., D. H. R. Barton, J. S. Fawcett, S. K. Knight, J. F. McGhie, M. K. Pradhan, and B. R. Thomas, *Chem. & Ind. (London)*, **1951**, 1067.
17. Barnes, C. S., D. H. R. Barton, A. R. H. Cole, J. S. Fawcett, and B. R. Thomas, *J. Chem. Soc.*, **1953**, 571.
18. Voser, W., M. V. Mijovic, O. Jeger, and L. Ruzicka, *Helv. Chim. Acta*, **34**, 1585 (1951).
19. Meystre, Ch., H. Frey, A. Wettstein, and K. Miescher, *Helv. Chim. Acta*, **27**, 1815 (1944).
20. Voser, W., H. H. Gunthard, O. Jeger, and L. Ruzicka, *Helv. Chim. Acta*, **35**, 66 (1952); Voser, W., O. Jeger, and L. Ruzicka, *Helv. Chim. Acta*, **35**, 497, 503 (1952).
21. Voser, W., M. V. Mijovic, H. Heusser, O. Jeger, and L. Ruzicka, *Helv. Chim. Acta*, **35**, 2414 (1952).
22. Curtis, R. G., J. Fridrichsons, and A. McL. Mathieson, *Nature*, **170**, 321 (1952).
23. Woodward, R. B., A. A. Patchett, D. H. R. Barton, D. A. J. Ives, and R. B. Kelly, *J. Am. Chem. Soc.*, **76**, 2852 (1954).
24. Conia, J-M., *Bull. soc. chim. France*, **1954**, 943.
25. Barton, D. H. R., *J. Chem. Soc.*, **1951**, 1444.

26. Bentley, H. R., J. A. Henry, D. S. Irvine, and F. S. Spring, *J. Chem. Soc.*, **1953**, 3673; Irvine, D. S., J. A. Henry, and F. S. Spring, *J. Chem. Soc.*, **1955**, 1316.

27. Cole, A. R. H., *J. Chem. Soc.*, **1954**, 3810.

28. Barton, D. H. R., J. E. Page, and E. W. Warnhoff, *J. Chem. Soc.*, **1954**, 2715.

29. Bentley, H. R., J. A. Henry, D. S. Irvine, D. Mukerji, and F. S. Spring, *J. Chem. Soc.*, **1955**, 596; Henry, J. A., D. S. Irvine, and F. S. Spring, *J. Chem. Soc.*, **1955**, 1607.

30. Holker, J. S. E., A. D. G. Powell, A. Robertson, J. J. H. Simes, R. S. Wright, and R. M. Gascoigne, *J. Chem. Soc.*, **1953**, 2422; Halsall, T. G., and R. Hodges, *J. Chem. Soc.*, **1954**, 2385; Bowers, A., T. G. Halsall, and G. C. Sayer, *J. Chem. Soc.*, **1954**, 3070; Guider, J. M., T. G. Halsall, R. Hodges, and E. R. H. Jones, *J. Chem. Soc.*, **1954**, 3234; Cort, L. A., R. M. Gascoigne, J. S. E. Holker, B. J. Ralph, A. Robertson, and J. J. Simes, *J. Chem. Soc.*, **1954**, 3713; Roth, M., G. Saucy, R. Anliker, O. Jeger, and H. Heusser, *Helv. Chim. Acta*, **36**, 1908 (1953).

31. Christen, K., M. Dunnenberger, C. B. Roth, H. Heusser, and O. Jeger, *Helv. Chim. Acta*, **35**, 1756 (1952).

32. Barton, D. H. R., J. F. McGhie, M. K. Pradhan, and S. A. Knight, *J. Chem. Soc.*, **1955**, 876.

33. Arigoni, D., R. Viterbo, M. Dunnenberger, O. Jeger, and L. Ruzicka, *Helv. Chim. Acta*, **37**, 2306 (1954).

34. Haines, D. W., and F. L. Warren, *J. Chem. Soc.*, **1949**, 2554; Barbour, J. B., R. N. E. Bennett, and F. L. Warren, *J. Chem. Soc.*, **1954**, 2540; and previous papers; cf. ref. 39.

35. Arigoni, D., O. Jeger, and L. Ruzicka, *Helv. Chim. Acta*, **38**, 222 (1955).

36. Barbour, J. B., W. A. Lourens, F. L. Warren, and K. H. Watling, *J. Chem. Soc.*, **1955**, 2194; cf. ref. 34.

37. Halsall, T. G., G. D. Meakins, and R. E. H. Swayne, *J. Chem. Soc.*, **1953**, 4139; Arigoni, D., H. Wyler, and O. Jeger, *Helv. Chim. Acta*, **37**, 1553 (1954).

38. Menard, E., H. Wyler, A. Hiestand, D. Arigoni, O. Jeger, and L. Ruzicka, *Helv. Chim. Acta*, **38**, 1517 (1955).

39. Warren, F. L., and K. H. Watling, *Chem. & Ind. (London)*, **1956**.

40. Dawson, M. C., T. G. Halsall, E. R. H. Jones, G. D. Meakins, and P. C. Phillips, *J. Chem. Soc.*, **1956**, 3172.

41. Lawrie, W., W. Hamilton, F. S. Spring, and H. S. Watson, *J. Chem. Soc.*, **1956**, 3272.

42. Barton, D. H. R., D. A. J. Ives, and B. R. Thomas, *J. Chem. Soc.*, **1955**, 2056.

43. Mills, J. S., and A. E. A. Werner, *J. Oil & Colour Chemists' Assoc.*, **37**, 131 (1954); Mills, J. S., and A. E. A. Werner, *Nature*, **169**, 1064 (1952).
44. Barton, D. H. R., and E. Seoane, *J. Chem. Soc.*, **1956**, 4150.
45. Mills, J. S., *J. Chem. Soc.*, **1956**, 2196.
46. Barton, D. H. R., and K. H. Overton, *J. Chem. Soc.*, **1955**, 2639.
47. Schaffner, K., R. Viterbo, D. Arigoni, and O. Jeger, *Helv. Chim. Acta*, **39**, 174 (1956).
48. Harvey, J., I. M. Heilbron (Sir), and E. D. Kamm, *J. Chem. Soc.*, **1926**, 3136.

CHAPTER 3

THE TRITERPENOIDS: II

THE β-AMYRIN GROUP

Elemi resin, when dissolved in alcohol, crystallises and gives a mixture of monohydric alcohols. This mixture was isolated as early as 1835, but serious investigation of the constituents did not begin until Vesterberg, in 1887, showed that the constituents could be separated after acetylation. He obtained two isomeric acetates, named α- and β-amyrin acetate, from which the related alcohols could be derived; these analysed for $C_{30}H_{50}O$.

The two amyrins are very widely distributed in the vegetable kingdom, both in the free state and as esters, together and separately. Amongst the sources of β-amyrin are holly bird-lime, shea nut fat, balata gum, gutta-percha, rice embryo, and the seeds and resins of grapes (Vitaceae) and alfalfa. Amongst the naturally occurring esters are the cinnamate, palmitate, and stearate; the myristate is present in the Javanese cocoa plant, whilst derivatives have also been found in tea leaves and camomile.

Early work did not reveal the presence of a double bond in β-amyrin. Bromination of the acetate, for instance, gave a substitution product rather than an addition compound (58), and it was therefore believed, to begin with, that β-amyrin was hexacyclic. Support for this seemed to come from attempted hydrogenation experiments, because at 280° ander a pressure of 80 atmospheres of hydrogen in the presence of platinum the alcohol was recovered unchanged.

From a study of the molecular refraction of the hydrocarbon ob-

tained by the dehydration of β-amyrin it was finally concluded that an unreactive double bond must be present, and this was confirmed by perbenzoic acid titrations. Furthermore, all β-amyrin derivatives gave yellow colours with tetranitromethane—a further indication of the presence of a double bond. The presence and location of the double bond was finally and rigidly established by the relationship demonstrated between β-amyrin and the related carboxylic acid derivative, oleanolic acid.

The skeleton assigned to the amyrins and their derivatives was, to a high degree, the outcome of dehydrogenation experiments. Amongst the products obtained were the compounds (I) → (VIII). Of these, sapotalene (III) has been isolated from a large number of similar triterpenoids. The formation of (IV) was believed to be due to the migration of a methyl group by a Wagner-Meerwein shift from a geminal position adjacent to the hydroxyl group. In confirmation of this β-amyrin was converted to the ketone and thence by Wolff-Kishner reduction to the hydrocarbon. Dehydrogenation of this gave no (IV), but another hydrocarbon (VIII) was isolated instead. The origin of these hydrocarbons in the presently accepted formula for β-amyrin (IX), that proposed originally by Haworth (1), is shown opposite.

These dehydrogenations also provided evidence for the position of the hydroxyl group. Evidence for this placing was also obtained by an oxidative degradation of another member of the β-amyrin series, hederagenin (X). The relation of this substance to β-amyrin was known, and during the degradation to be described the double bond and the carboxyl group were protected by lactone formation

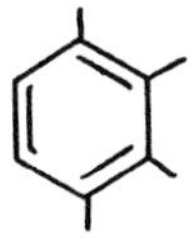
(I)

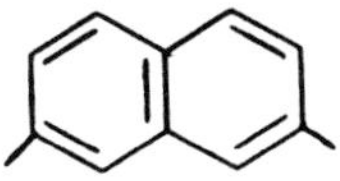
(II)

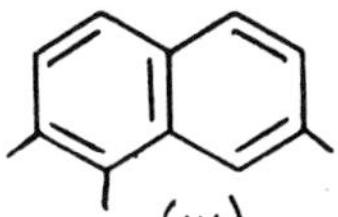
(III)

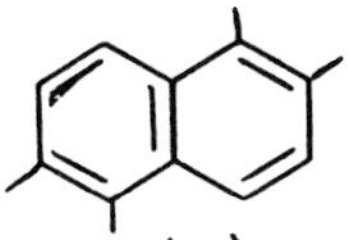
(IV)

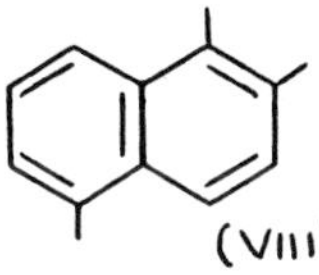
(VIII)

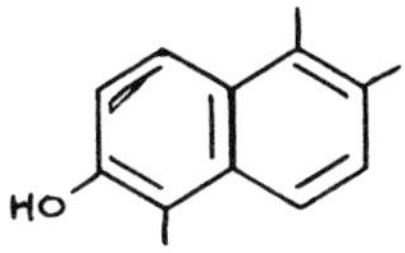
(V)

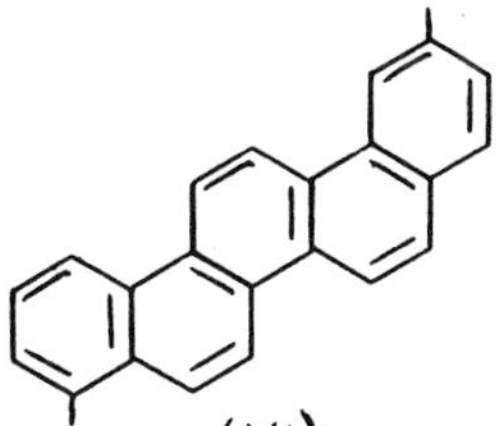
(VI)

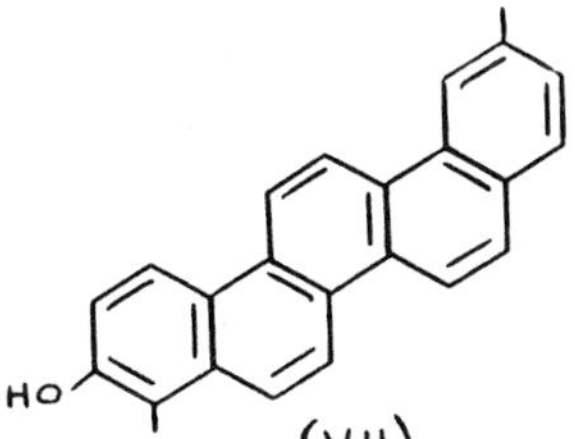
(VII)

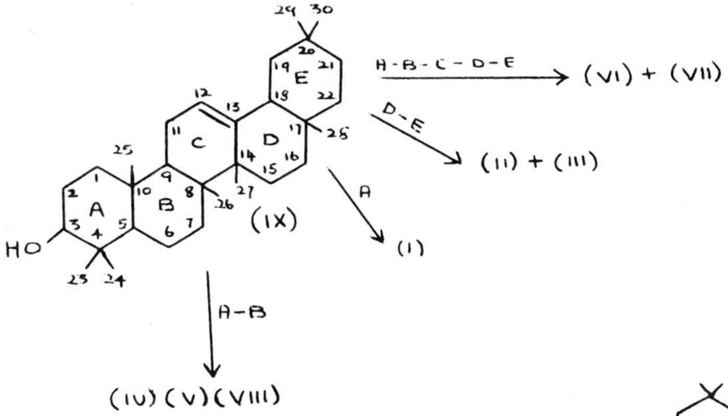

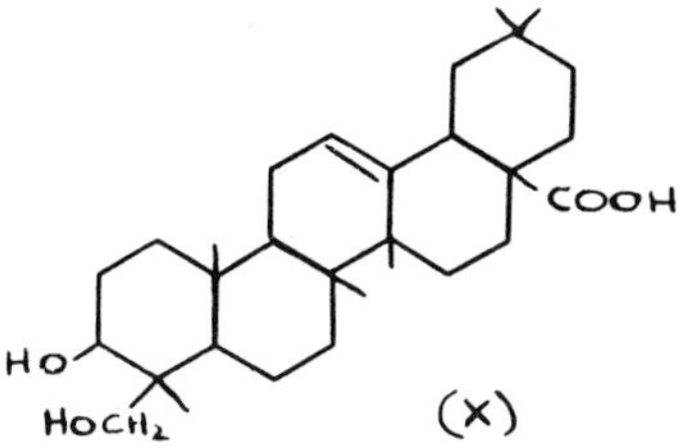

(X)

(XI). In the β-amyrin series where a carboxyl group is present at C_{17}, such lactonisation may be facile; it is catalysed by acid.

This complex series of degradative steps (2) and the properties and degree of substitution of the acids formed lead to the conclusion that the hydroxyl group is at C_3, and that there is a methyl group at C_{10} but not at C_5. In addition the terminal rings in β-amyrin, oleanolic acid, and related compounds, undergo with phosphorus pentachloride the ring contraction common to all such compounds having the appropriate stereochemistry (see page 78).

Another group of chemical reactions is centred on the only other chemically accessible part of the molecule, the double bond. When β-amyrin acetate is oxidised with potassium persulphate or with

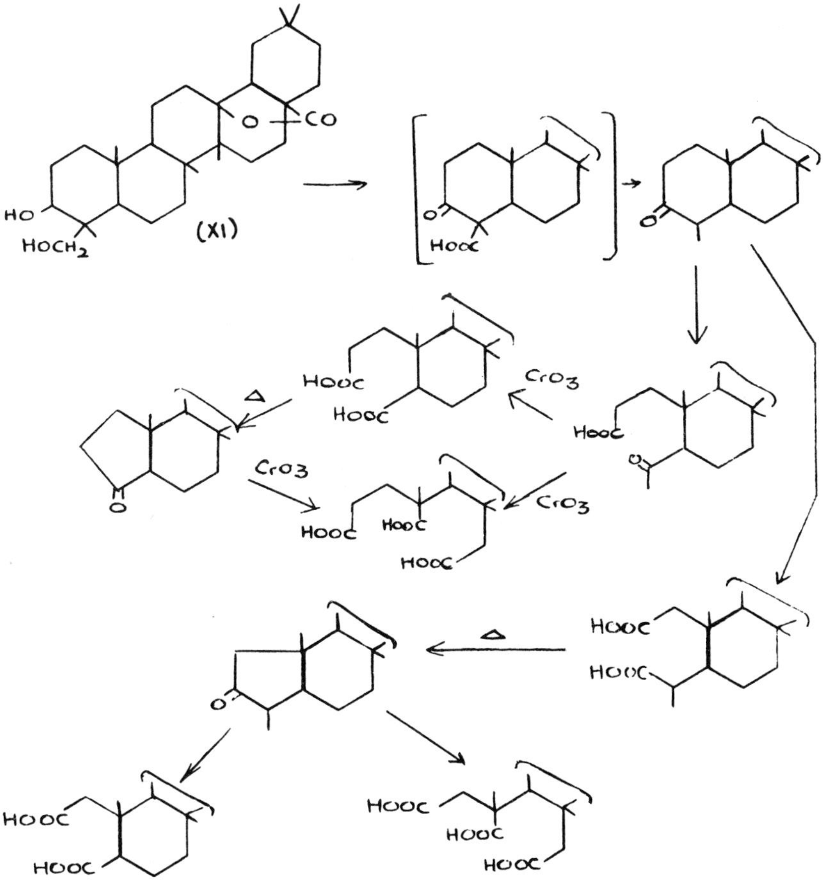
HO
HOCH₂
(XI)
CO
HOOC
CrO₃
Δ
HOOC
HOOC
HOOC
HOOC
HOOC
HOOC
HOOC
HOOC
HOOC
HOOC

hydrogen peroxide in acetic acid, a ketone is obtained, β-amyranonyl acetate (XII).*

The ketone is also obtained by the action of perbenzoic and monoperphthalic acids, possibly through an intermediate oxide. The ketone could be reduced by the Wolff-Kishner method to the saturated alcohol β-amyranol (XIII). When (XII) was treated with fuming nitric acid at $0°$ and then at $50°$ a dicarboxylic acid was obtained (XIV). On heating, the anhydride of this gave a ketone (XV). Now, whereas the carbonyl group of (XII) showed a band in the infra-red at 1700 cm^{-1}, that of (XV) had a band at 1735 cm^{-1}, which meant that they were in six- and five-membered rings respectively. The double bond itself was, therefore, in a six-membered ring. Further, since the formation of (XIV) did not involve the loss of any carbon atoms the double bond must be flanked by a methylene group (3). This was confirmed by chromic acid oxidation of β-amyrin acetate when allylic oxidation takes place to give β-amyrenonyl acetate (XVII) ($\lambda_{max.}$ 249 mμ). Hydrogenation of (XVII) gives, by hydrogenolysis, perhaps, of an intermediate allylic alcohol, β-amyrin acetate. These reactions may be summarised in the partial formula (XVIII). There were, however, reasons for expanding this formula. Reduction of (XVII) with sodium and ethanol gave an adduct, possibly (XVI), in which one molecule of ethyl alcohol was incorporated. A similar adduct was obtained if amyl alcohol was used, and both of these when heated with sodium acetate and acetic anhydride lost the alcohol to give the diene (XIX) ($\lambda_{max.}$ 281 mμ). This diene must, from its ultra-violet spectrum, contain both double bonds in one ring, and so the deducible partial formula may be expanded to (XX). The same diene (XIX) is produced from the lithium aluminum hydride reduction of (XVII) followed by dehydration with acetic anhydride and a trace of acid. In this reaction the above diene is accompanied by an isomeric heteroannular diene. By the action of bromine in glacial acetic acid on the benzoate corresponding to (XVII), by a process of bromination and dehydrobromination, an additional double bond is introduced at the 18:19 position to

---

*A systematic system of nomenclature based on the saturated hydrocarbon derived from β-amyrin is also used. This skeleton is termed oleanane, and on this system the ketone is 3-acetoxy-12-oxo-oleanane.

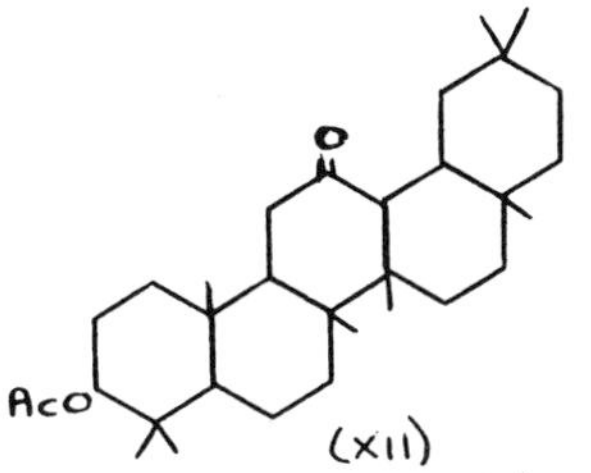

(XII)

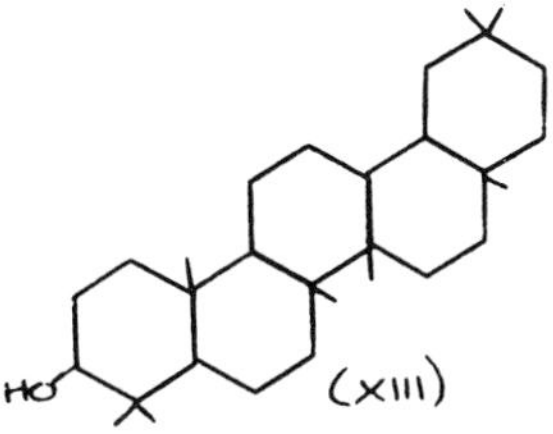

(XIII)

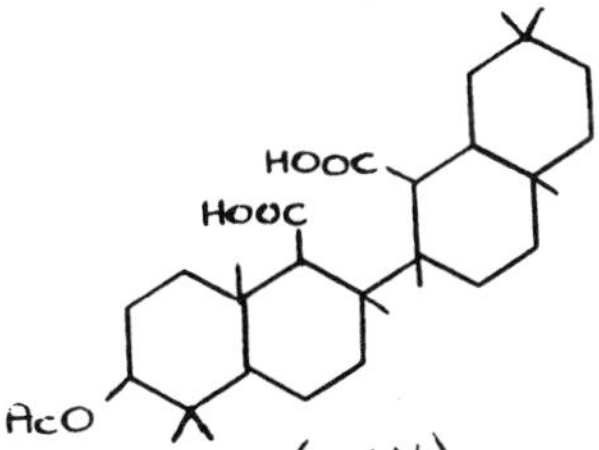

(XIV)

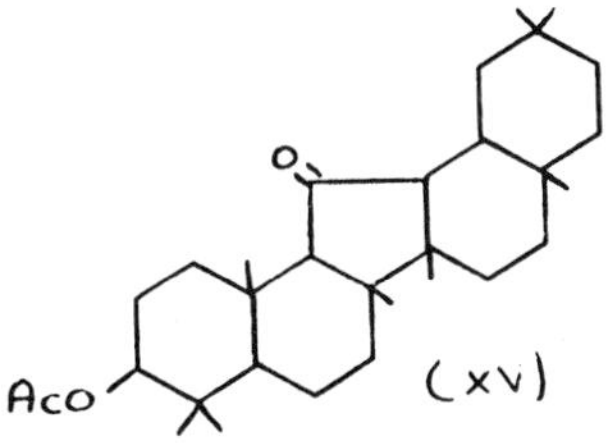

(XV)

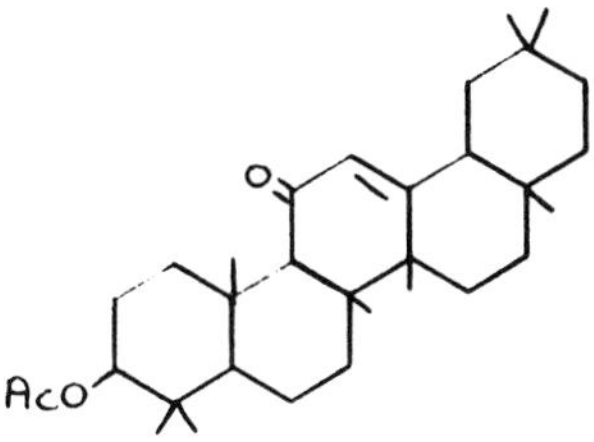

(XVII)

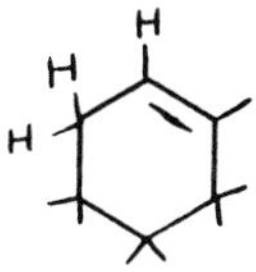

(XVIII)

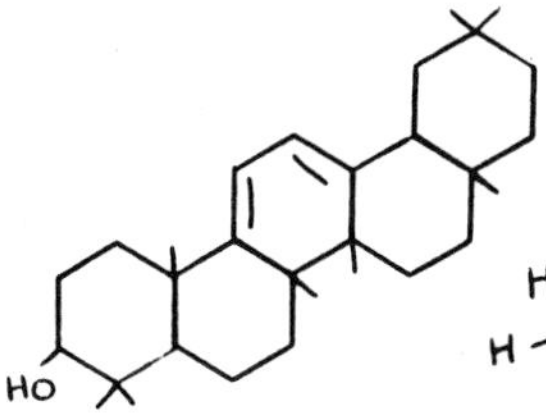

(XIX)

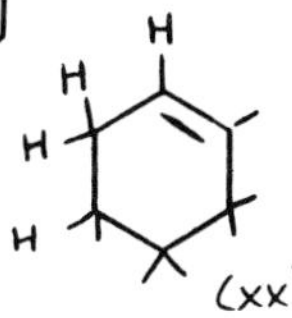

(XX)

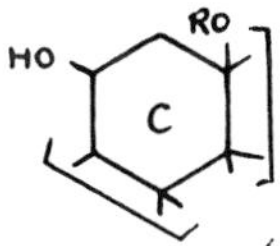

(XVI)

give (XXI). Further information regarding the environment of the double bond derives from the reactions summarised opposite. The acetate (XXIII) is that of olean-13 : 18-ene; it is also known as δ-amyrin acetate. The 13 : 18 position is that most stable for the double bond, but when substances in which the double bond is in another position (e.g., 12 : 13) are isomerised the product obtained always contains equilibrium proportions of other isomers as well as the 13 : 18 (4). Whilst these experiments, together with the dehydrogenation evidence, made the above structure (IX) for β-amyrin probable, evidence had still to be presented for the location of the double bond. This was obtained by the study of a related member of the

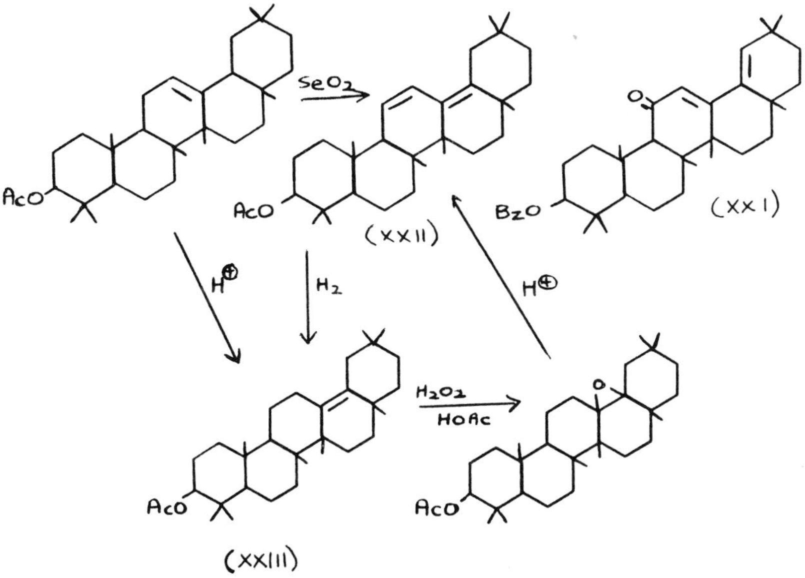
AcO
SeO2
AcO
(XXII)
BzO
(XXI)
H⊕
H2
H⊕
H2O2
HOAc
O
AcO
AcO
(XXIII)

β-amyrin group—oleanolic acid (XXIV) (5a). The conversion of the carboxyl group in this substance by standard methods into methyl gives β-amyrin. A common pathway lies through the acid chloride and Rosenmund reduction, followed by Wolff-Kishner reduction. Oxidation of the derived ketone (56) of oleanolic acid, followed by methylation and partial hydrolysis, gives the methyl ester of iso-oleanonic acid lactone dicarboxylic acid (XXV). Pyrolysis of this gives products representing rings A and B and rings D and E.

These reactions show clearly that the double bond in oleanolic acid, and therefore in β-amyrin, is in the centre ring. Pyrolysis of the dimethyl ester of (XXV) and separation taking advantage of the carbonyl group gave the substance (XXVI). Removal of the carbonyl group then gave (XXVII), a substance also obtained (page 74) by the degradation of ambrein. The relationship of the latter to manool and to dehydroabietic acid establishes rigidly the structure of rings A and B in oleanolic acid.

The non-ketonic fraction produced in the above pyrolysis, a mixture of esters, was hydrolysed to the acids. These on selenium dehydrogenation gave 2 : 7-dimethylnaphthalene and (XXVIII); the structure of the latter was proven by synthesis. Palladised charcoal dehydrogenation of the ester mixture gave, after hydrolysis, (XXIX). The structure of this, while not confirmed by synthesis, received support from its ultra-violet spectrum which was very similar to that of 2 : 3 : 6-trimethylbenzoic acid (5b).

This additional evidence is adequate to establish the structure of β-amyrin, but much confirmation has been obtained in various ways. The relative positions of the ethylenic linkage and the carboxyl group in oleanolic acid were suggested by the following evidence. In the presence of acids such as hydrogen chloride oleanolic acid

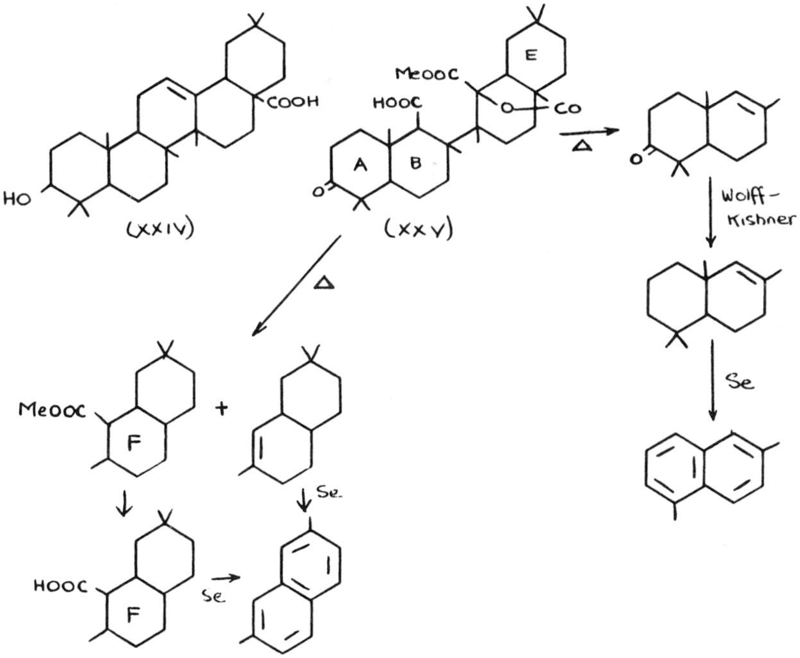

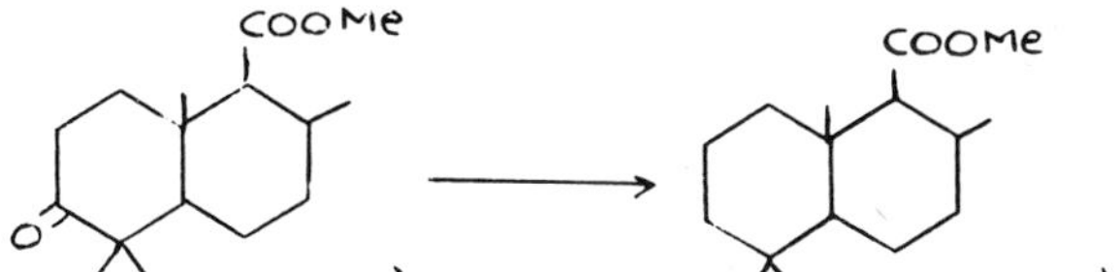

(XXVI) (XXVII)

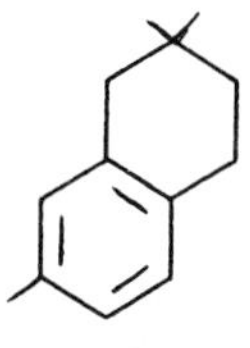

(XXVIII)

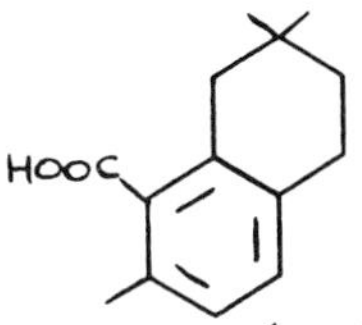

(XXIX)

is converted into a lactone (XXX) the infra-red spectrum of which indicates it to be a γ-lactone. With bromine a bromolactone is obtained (XXXI), presumably as shown in the part formula (XXXII). This, too, is a γ-lactone and may be reduced (XXXIII) back to the original acid. This is strong evidence for the placing of the carboxyl group on the β-carbon atom with respect to the more substituted end of the double bond to allow Markownikoff protonation (or bromination) prior to cyclisation. By the action of acid oleanolic acid derivatives may be isomerised at the 18 position to give 18-*iso* products in which the ring junction between D and E is changed from *cis* to *trans*.

By the oxidation of β-amyrin acetate, δ-amyrin acetate, and a number of other derivatives with selenium dioxide a diene-dione

(xxx)

(xxxi)

(xxxii)

(xxxiii)

(XXXIV) is obtained (6). This gives with hydrazine the pyridazine (XXXV) and, on reduction with zinc dust in ethanol, gives (XXXVI) which has the absorption of an unsaturated ketone ($\lambda_{max.}$ 246 mμ). This is strong evidence for the constitution of (XXXIV) which is supported by that provided by other transformations. The equivalent conversion to (XXXVII) takes place in the oleanolic acid series, and the constitution of (XXXVII) is supported by much the same evidence. In addition (XXXVII) has been related to a triterpenoid of known constitution, siaresinolic acid (XXXVIII), by the scheme shown (7). The acid (XXXIX) corresponding to (XXXVII) loses carbon dioxide on heating (5c) by virtue of its nature as a $\beta:\gamma$-unsaturated acid. The product (XL) also gave a pyridazine (XLI) by reaction with hydrazine. Oxidation of (XXXVII) with

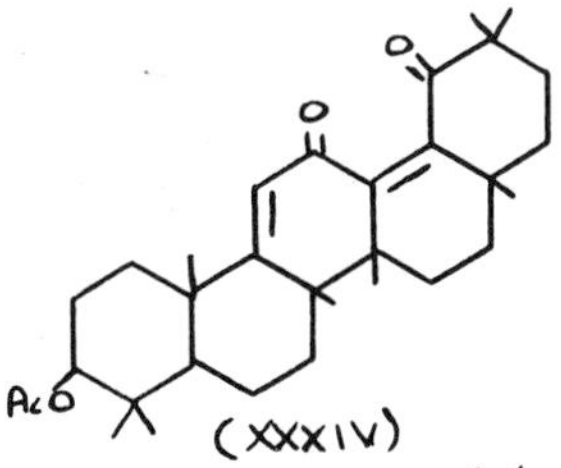

(XXXIV)

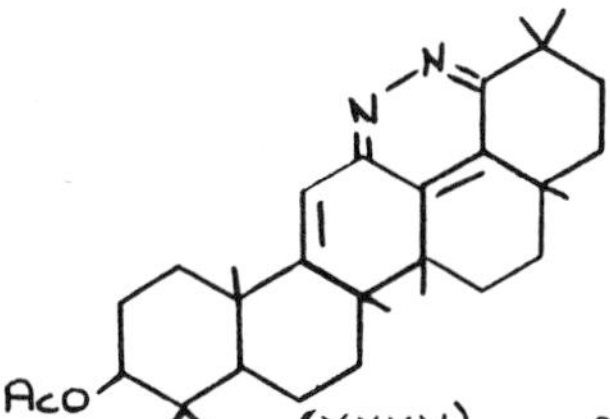

(XXXV)

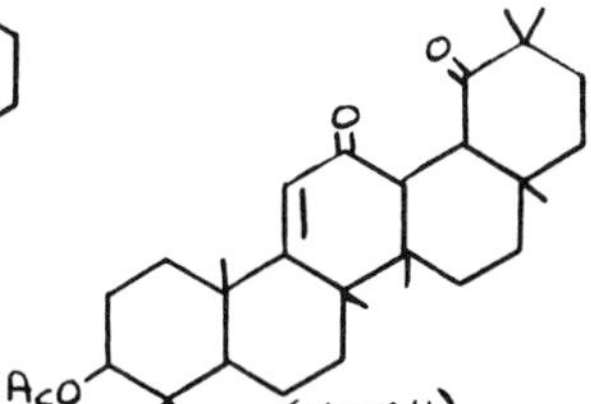

(XXXVI)

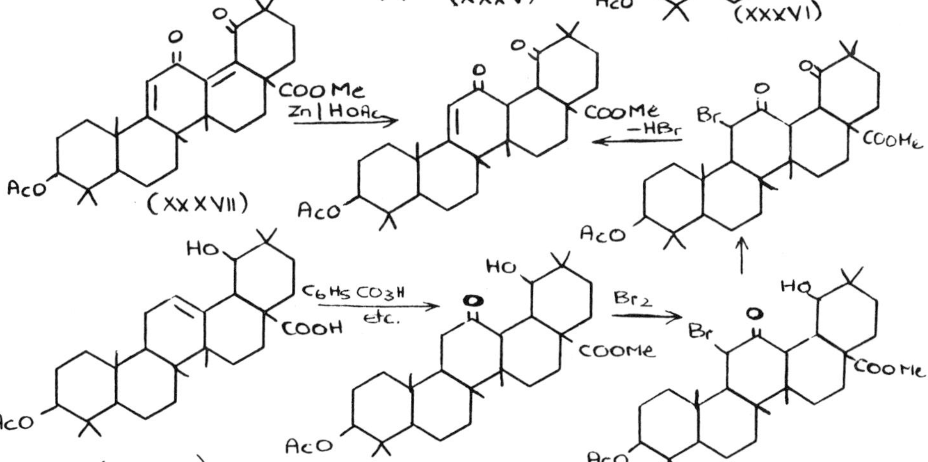

(XXXVII)

(XXXVIII)

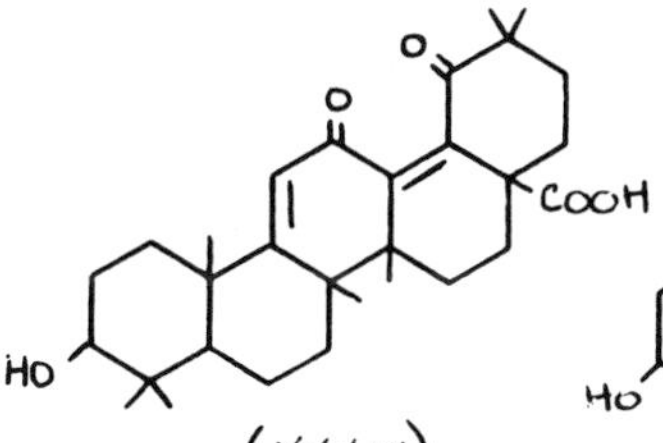

(XXXIX)

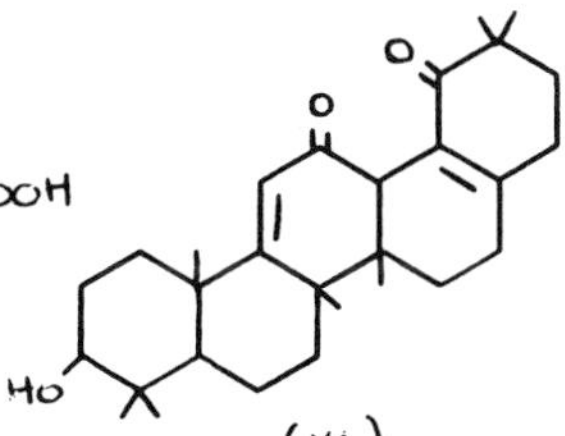

(XL)

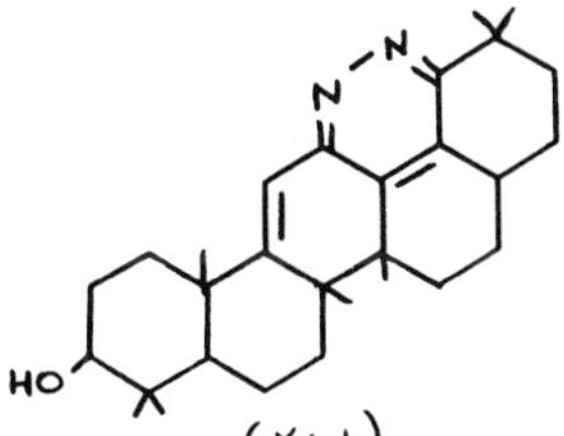

(XLI)

chromic acid gave an oxide (XLII) formulated in this way because vigorous alkaline hydrolysis gave, probably through the mechanism shown, a *nor* acid (XLIII) containing a β-diketone grouping.

Yet more evidence for the relationship of the carboxyl and double bond was obtained in a simple way from dehydro-oleanolic acid (XLIX, R = H) ($\lambda_{max.}$ 250 mμ). Pyrolysis of this results in decarboxylation and movement out of conjugation of one of the double bonds to give (XLV). This reaction proceeds through a cyclic transition state (XLIV) (8). The carboxyl must be, therefore, attached to a carbon atom α to one end of the heteroannular system.

This evidence, taken altogether, establishes beyond doubt the gross structure of β-amyrin, oleanolic acid, and related compounds. There is a wealth of other work to support this.

The following discussion, which relates to the stereochemistry of β-amyrin and of oleanolic acid, is not intended as a rigid proof, but rather as an indication of the methods by which such complex problems are solved. In this particular case the complete structure was also, later, determined by X-ray analysis.

The production of the bicyclic carboxylic acid ester (XXVII) from the pyrolysis of an oleanolic acid derivative and its correlation with ambrein, manool, and abietic acid establishes that rings A and B are *trans*-fused. The retropinacolic change, by the action of

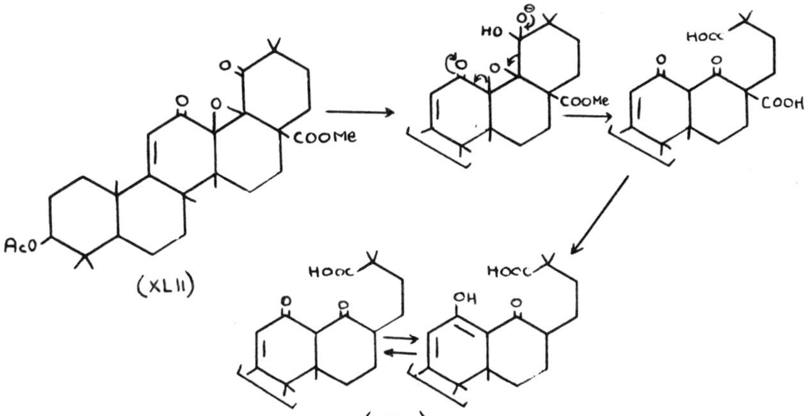

(XLII)

(XLIII)

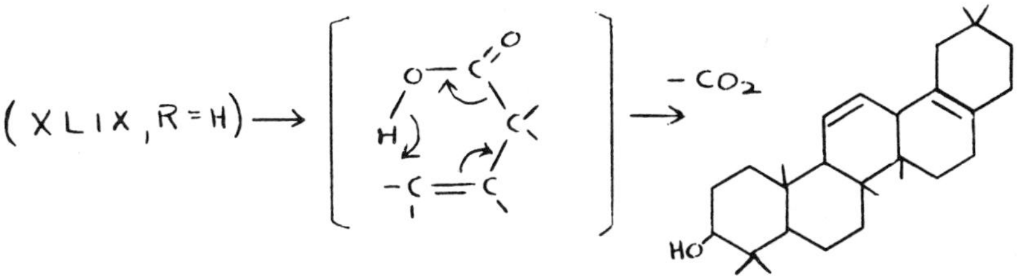

$$(XLIX, R=H) \rightarrow \left[\quad \right] \xrightarrow{-CO_2}$$

(XLIV)

(XLV)

phosphorus pentachloride on the alcohol, further confirms the part structure (XLVI).

The carboxyl group at C_{17} must be axial for lactone formation, but this does not differentiate between *cis*- and *trans*-fused D/E junctions. Methyl 11-keto-oleanolate acetate (XLVII) can, by treatment with alkali, be converted to an isomer (XLVIII) having the same chromophore in the ultra-violet. This isomer must differ from (XLVII) at C_9 and/or C_{18}. Hydrogenation removes the keto group giving an isomer of methyl oleanolate acetate. Since selenium dioxide on this isomer gave methyl dehydro-oleanolate acetate (XLIX; R = Me acetate instead of alcohol), the centre at which isomerisation took place was removed in the formation of the 13:18 double bond. (XLVIII) therefore differs from (XLVII) only in the configuration of C_{18}. This requires that the D/E junction be in the unstable *cis* fusion.

The same conclusion may be reached as follows. The hydroxyl group in siaresinolic acid, because of its resistance to esterification and its ease of elimination towards C_{18}, as in (L) to (LI), must be axial. Further, the hydrogen at C_{18} must be *trans* to it, for the easy four-centre planar transition state. But if the carboxyl at C_{17} and the hydroxyl at C_{19} are both axial yet do not lactonise they should be on opposite sides of the molecule as represented in (L). The hydrogen at C_{18} is therefore on the *same* side of the molecule as the C_{17} carboxyl. Oxidation of methyl dihydrosiaresinolate acetate to the ketone (LII) followed by treatment with base again leads to epimerisation at C_{18} and the formation of (LIII). This evidence confirms previous conclusions.

The relationship of the centres C_{17} and C_{18} to the adjoining centres was established by the study of another triterpenoid acid,

(XLVI)   (XLVII)   (XLVIII)

(XLIX)

(L)   (LI)   (LII)   (LIII)

morolic acid (LIV). This substance differs from the β-amyrin series in possessing a double bond at the $18:19$ position rather than at the $12:13$ (8). The proof of its constitution is not of immediate concern, but after its deduction the proposed structure was partially synthesised from siaresinolic acid. The immediately relevant feature of its chemistry is its conversion through the diol diacetate (LV) to the oxide (LVI) and to norolean-$16:18$-dienyl acetate (LVII) by the mechanism shown. In this sequence of reactions it should be noted that the configuration at C_{13} is unaffected, and so must be as in morolic acid itself. Now the compound (LVII) may also be derived from siaresinolic acid as shown. In the decarboxylative step from (LVIII) to (LIX) through the cyclic transition state (XLIV) it follows that the hydrogen deposited at C_{13}, with concomitant migration of the double bond, must be on the same side of the molecule as the carboxyl group and axial in conformation. The configuration of the hydrogen atom at C_{13} in morolic acid is thus the same as that of the carboxyl group. Since the configuration of the carboxyl group in morolic acid is the same as that in siaresinolic acid, that is β, it follows that the hydrogen at C_{13} in the former is likewise β. The configuration at C_{13} in morolic acid being known, it is now required to know whether it is in the stable or unstable configuration. Its partial synthesis (10) from siaresinolic acid is shown opposite. Since this involves the treatment of the ketone (LX) with strong base during the Wolff-Kishner, it follows that it is the

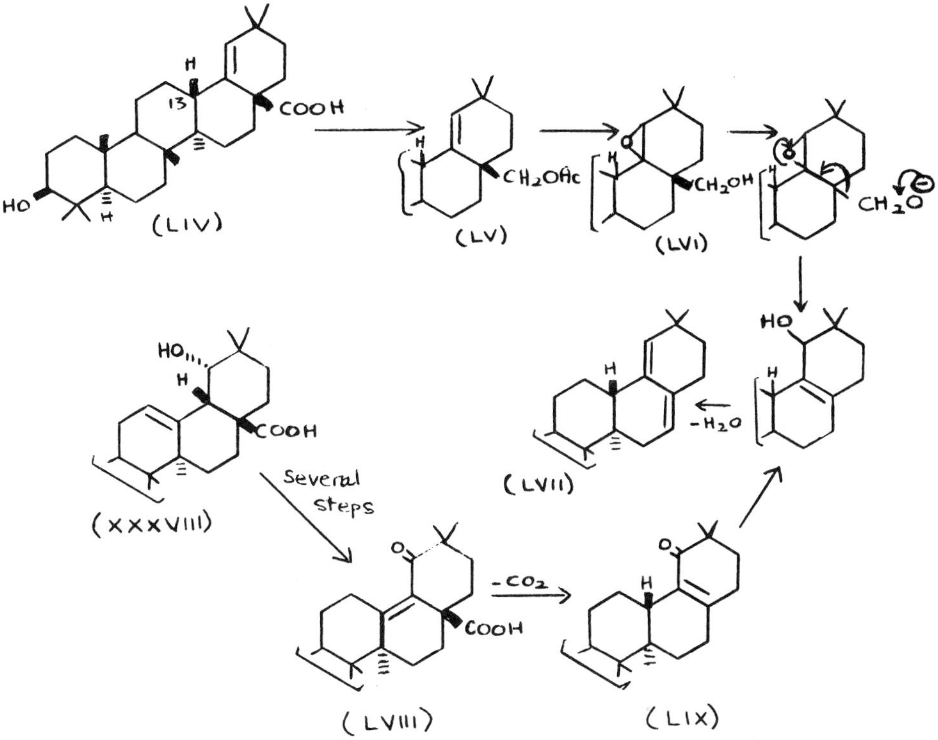

(LIV)
COOH
CH2OAc
(LV)
CH2OH
(LVI)
CH2O
HO
(LVII)
-H2O
(XXXVIII)
Several steps
-CO2
COOH
(LVIII)
(LIX)

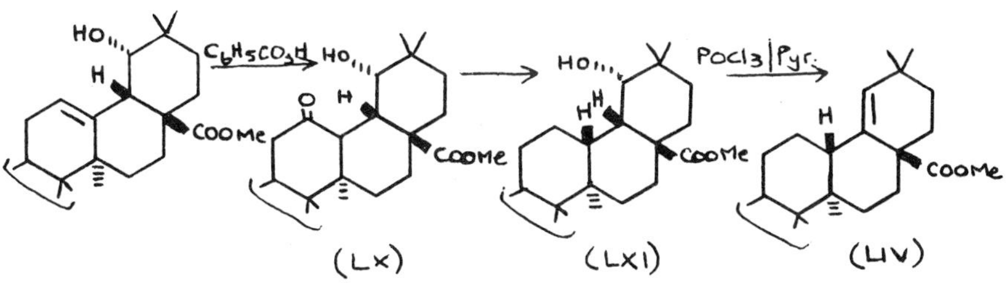

C6H5CO3H
COOMe
POCl3|Pyr.
(LX)
(LXI)
(LIV)

stable configuration. It is now possible to deduce the configuration at C_{14}.

From a consideration of non-bonded interactions, as applied to perhydrophenanthrenes, and as a result of direct experimentation, certain conclusions have been reached regarding stabilities (9). Relevant amongst these is the study of the compounds represented by (LXII), (LXIV), (LXIII), and (LXV). Here (LXII) is more stable than (LXIII), and (LXIV) more stable than (LXV). Now since in rings C, D, and E of (LXI) the configuration at C_{13} is *stable* and *syn* to that at C_{18}, a choice, necessarily between (LXIII) and (LXIV), must be for (LXIV); C_{14} is therefore α. This centre has the same configuration in all this series of compounds, and so the stereochemistry so far deduced with regard to rings C, D, and E in oleanolic acid is represented in the formulation (LXVI). It should be noted that the stability argument has been assumed to be extendable to cases in which the bridgehead hydrogen has been replaced by a methyl group. It was shown (page 146) that methyl 11-keto-oleanolate acetate (XLVII) with base epimerised at C_{18} *only* and not at C_9. From this it must be concluded that rings B and C are fused in a stable configuration. In (LXI), then, ring C is fused both to ring B and ring D by a *stable* junction. Hence, from the work on perhydrophenanthrenes already referred to it may be concluded that ring C is in a chair conformation. By the steps outlined below, in which C_{13} remains in the stable fusion, (LXVII) has been converted into (LXVIII). This substance is considered to have an axial hydroxyl group for three reasons. Firstly, because it resists acylation; secondly, because of its ease of elimination to give (LXIX); and thirdly because lithium aluminium hydride reductions of hindered ketones are known to give axial alcohols. The hindered nature of the ketone at C_{11} is shown by its non-elimination under Wolff-Kishner conditions. If the hydroxyl in (LXVIII) is axial then, since ring C is a chair, it must be on the same side as the axial hydrogen at C_{13}—that is, β. Furthermore, because of facile *trans* elimination to give (LXIX) the hydrogen at C_9 must be α and axial. This suggests the expression (LXX) as the stereochemistry so far deduced for oleananolic acid (59). Viewed in another way, if

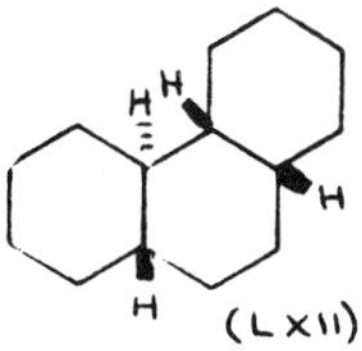

(LXII)

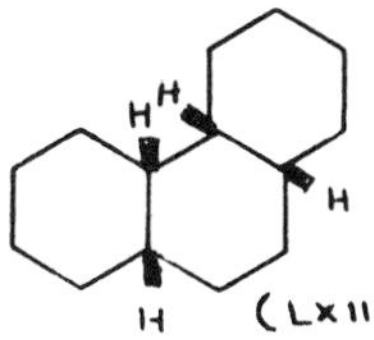

(LXIII)

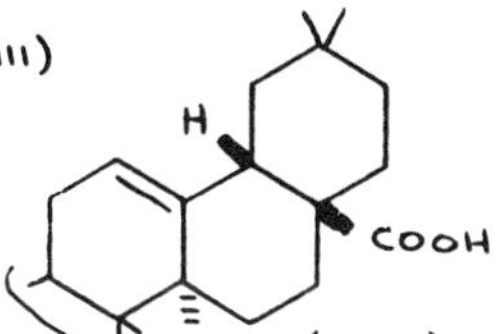

(LXVI)
COOH

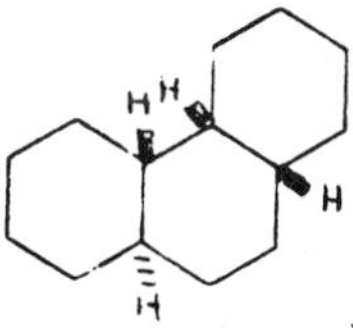

(LXIV)

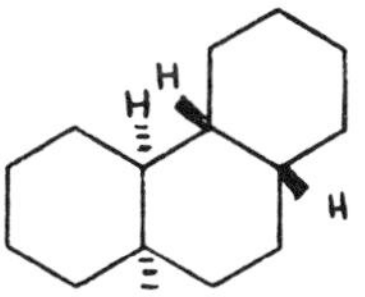

(LXV)

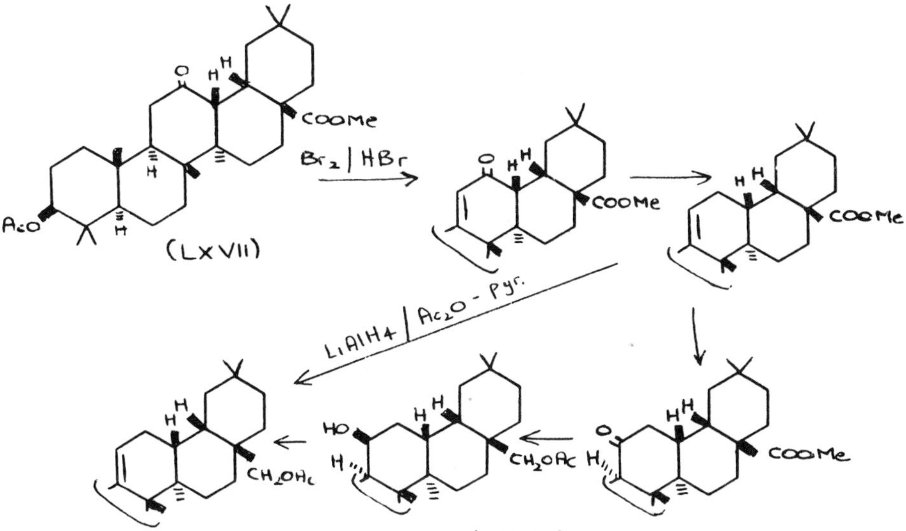

(LXVII)
AcO
COOMe
Br_2/HBr

COOMe

COOMe

$LiAlH_4/Ac_2O - Pyr.$

(LXIX)
CH_2OH_c

(LXVIII)
HO
CH_2OAc

$COOMe$
O

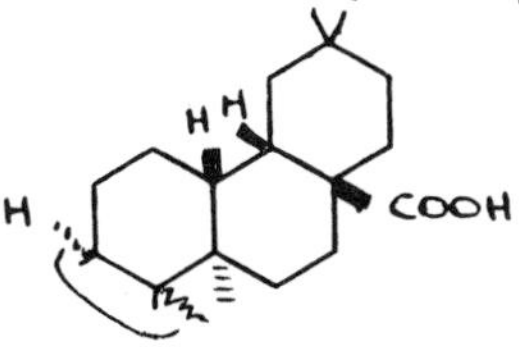

(LXX)
COOH

both C_9 and C_{13} are to have the more stable configuration analogy with the known stabilities of perhydrophenanthrenes with a *trans* fusion suggests that C_8 may be α or β, but that C_9 must be α—that is, *trans-anti-trans* or *cis-syn-trans*. (LXX) is an expression of both theses.

Since the A/B ring fusion is known to be *trans*, these rings may be attached to the remainder of the molecule in four ways (LXXIa–d) in which C_9 is α. Of these, (c) represents an unstable fusion because it requires a boat ring B; (b) can be constructed with all-chair rings, but then $C_9(\alpha)$ is equatorial; only (a) and (d) remain. These may be represented in the full stereoformulae (LXXII A and B). Decision between these two was chemically not possible, but molecular rotation arguments supported (LXXIIA), and showed the absolute configuration to be the same as in the steroids (11). The relative stereochemistry has since been shown by X-ray studies (12) of methyl oleanolate iodoacetate, and the absolute configuration by direct correlation. This leads to (LXXIII) as the representation of β-amyrin.

Compounds of the β-amyrin–oleanolic acid series appear to be the most widespread of the pentacyclic triterpenoids. Apart from those already mentioned a large number are known which have functional groups elsewhere, or in addition to those present in the parent system. An oxygen function at C_3, however, appears to be ubiquitous. This is not always present as a hydroxyl group, and in the compound icterogenin (LXXIV) (23) it is replaced by a ketonic function. This leads to the interesting dealdolisation to give (LXXV), which takes place when icterogenin is treated with alkali under mild conditions. This particular reaction may conceivably be associated with its reported physiological activity in sheep. By disturbing the digestive process, icterogenin is said to induce the passage of phylloerythrin (from chlorophyll) into the blood system and so to cause light sensitivity.

It is impossible here to describe the extensive work which has gone into the elucidation of the many members of the β-amyrin group. Table 2 lists a number of these compounds together with their functional groups and sources.

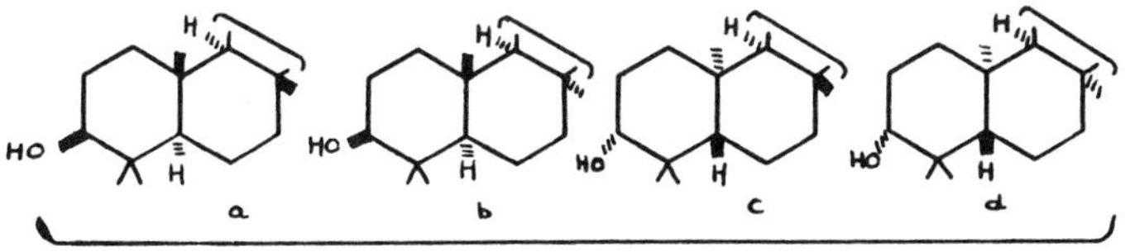

(LXXI)

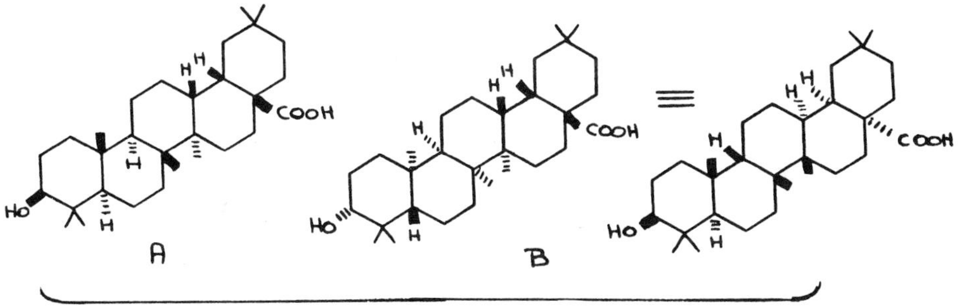

(LXXII)

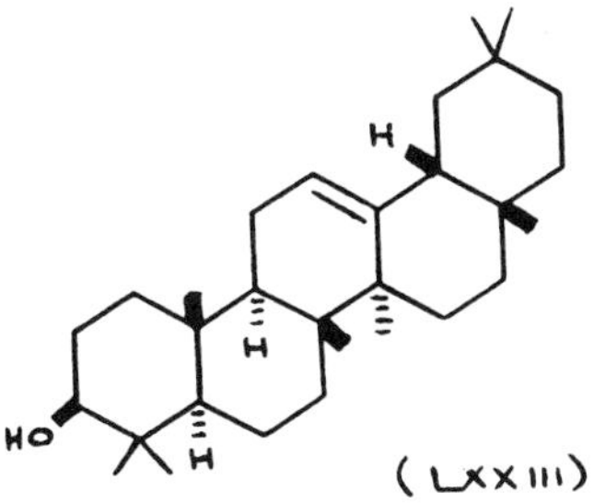

(LXXIII)

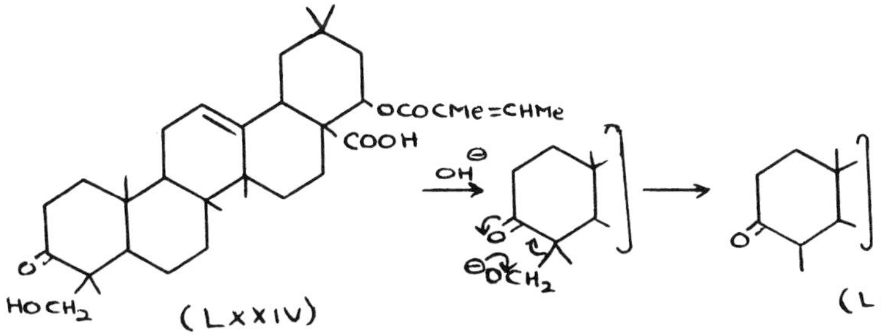

(LXXIV)

(LXXV)

TABLE 2

Naturally Occurring Compounds of the β-Amyrin Series

Compound	Source	Functional Group	Ref.
Arjunolic acid	*Terminalia arjuna*	(LXXVI)	13
Barringtogenol	*Barringtonia racemosa*	(LXXVII)	14
α-Boswellic acid	Olibanum	3 (*epi*) OH; 4-COOH	15
Echinocystic acid	*Echinocystis fabacea*	16α-OH; 17-COOH	16
Erythrodiol	Fruit of *Erythroxylon novogranatense*	28-OH	17
Genin A	Roots of *Primula officinalis*	16-OH; 28-OH	18
Germanicol	Latex of *Lactuca virosa*	(LXXX)	19
Glycyrrhetic acid	Liquorice root	(LXXVIII)	20
Gypsogenin	Fuller's herb	4-CHO; 17-COOH	21
Hederagenin	Ivy; soap nuts	(X)	22
Icterogenin	*Lippia rehmanni*	(LXXIV)	23
Lantadene B	*Lantana camera*	(LXXXI)	24
Maniladiol	Manila elemi resin	16-*epi*-OH	25
Morolic acid	*Mora excelsa* Benth.	(LIV)	8
Oleanolic acid	Sugar beet, clove buds	(XXIV)	
Quillaic acid	Quillaia bark	16-OH; 4-CHO; 17-COOH	26
Rehmannic acid (Lantadene A)	*Lippia rehmanni* *Lantana camera*	As (LXXXI), but with angelic acid	27
Siaresinolic acid	Siam Gum Benzoin	(XXXVIII)	
Sumaresinolic acid	Sumatra Gum Benzoin	6-OH; 17-COOH	28
Terminolic acid	*Terminalia ivorensis*	(LXXIX)	29

In addition, separate mention must be made of the extensive investigation of cacti carried out by Djerassi and his co-workers. These authors have succeeded in isolating, characterising, and elucidating the structures and stereochemistry of a large number of triterpenoids from these sources. Those belonging to this series are described in Table 3.

(LXXVI)

(LXXVII)

(LXXVIII)

(LXXIX)

(LXXX)

(LXXXIa)

(LXXXI)

TABLE 3

Cactus Triterpenoids of the β-Amyrin Group (30)

Compound	Source	Functional Group
Cochalic acid	*Myrtillocactus cochal*	16β-OH; 17-COOH
Dumortierigenin	*Lemaireocereus dumortieri*	(LXXXIa)
Gummosogenin	*Machaerocereus gummosus*	16β-OH; 17-CHO
Longispinogenin	*Lemaireocereus longispinus*	16β-OH; 28-OH
Machaeric acid	*Machaerocereus gummosus*	21-Oxo; 17-COOH
Machaerinic acid	*Machaerocereus gummosus*	21-OH; 17-COOH
Queretaroic acid	*Lemaireocereus queretaroensis*	30-OH; 17-COOH

In addition to the substances listed in Tables 2 and 3 there are a number of substances of modified structure related to β-amyrin. Some are discussed in the following chapter.

Much of the so far described triterpenoid chemistry might be said to be unexceptional as far as mechanism is concerned. The triterpenoids are, none the less, capable of complex transformations comparable to those of the more interesting sesquiterpenoids. Available space permits only a single illustration.

A frequently encountered oxidation product of β-amyrin was a substance $C_{32}H_{46}O_5$ generally referred to as the "O_5-acetate." Some of its various geneses are shown opposite.

The O_5-acetate gives a faint yellow colour with tetranitromethane, no colouration with ferric chloride, and contains no active hydrogen. It has $\lambda_{max.}$ 230 mμ. Recent investigations by McKean and Spring (31) have established its structure as (LXXXII), largely on the basis of the transformations illustrated. It has been proposed that the genesis of this remarkable compound proceeds through the triketone (LXXXIII) (32).

THE α-AMYRIN GROUP

α-Amyrin forms the main triterpenoid component of the latex from the milk tree (*Brosium galactodendron*). There are numerous other sources of which the most useful is Manila elemi resin. Here it occurs together with β-amyrin from which it can best be separated

(LXXXII)

(LXXXIII)

by crystallisation of the benzoates. α-Amyrin is contained in the beverage known as maté.

The chemistry of α-amyrin has not yet reached its final stage, though active work in the field makes it likely that it will soon do so. It has a considerable general resemblance to β-amyrin in its properties, and the similarity is reflected in the dehydrogenation products. In the early stages their properties appeared so similar that α- and β-amyrin were thought to be stereoisomers.

Evidence that this was not so was obtained by the series of reactions shown opposite.

α-Amyrin (LXXXIV) is converted to the ketone (LXXXV) by the action of ozone followed by acid or by the action of perhydrol and acetic acid. The double bond is more resistant than that in β-amyrin for α-amyrin is unaffected by perbenzoic acid. The products of pyrolysis of the ester (LXXXVII) (33) were separated taking advantage of the carbonyl function and using the Girard reagent. The ester (XXVII) was identical with that obtained by the degrada- of oleanolic acid. Rings A and B of α-amyrin were therefore as in β-amyrin. The final product obtained from the non-ketonic portion was sapotalene (LXXXVI). Since the equivalent product obtained from β-amyrin had been 2 : 7-dimethylnaphthalene this suggested a different disposition of the methyl groups in ring E.

It must be mentioned here that an alternative structure (LXXXVIII) has been proposed (34) for α-amyrin. With this structure it is necessary to assume that expansion of ring E takes place during dehydrogenation. While this in itself is feasible, a model substance (35) is available in novic acid identical in rings D and E

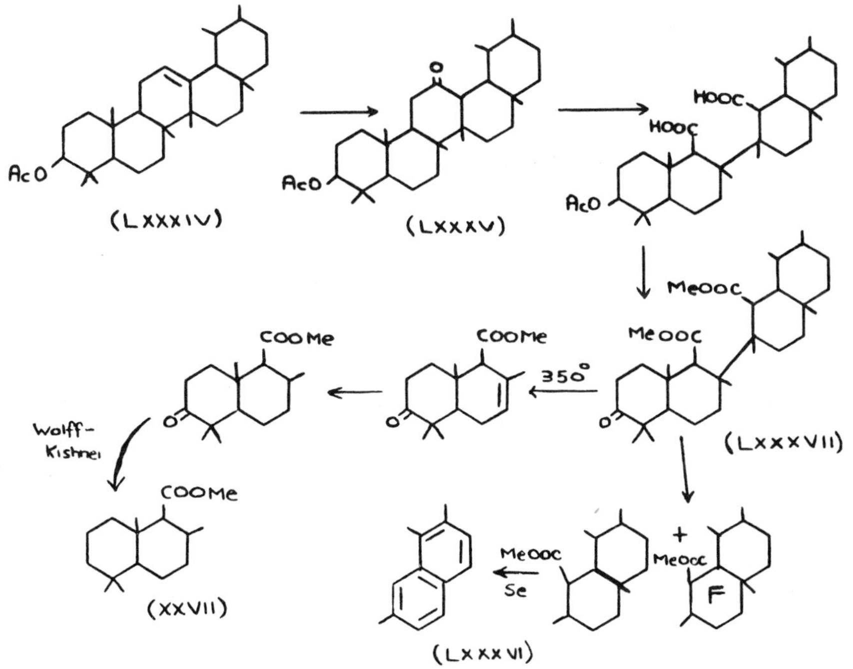

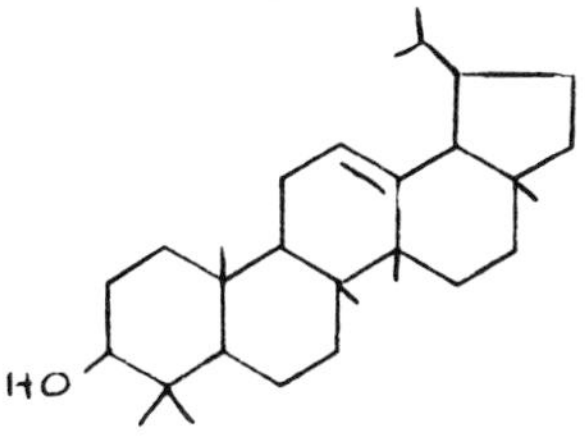

(LXXXIV)

(LXXXV)

(LXXXVII)

(LXXXVI)

(XXVII)

Wolff-
Kishner

350°

MeOOC

Se

+

F

(LXXXVIII)

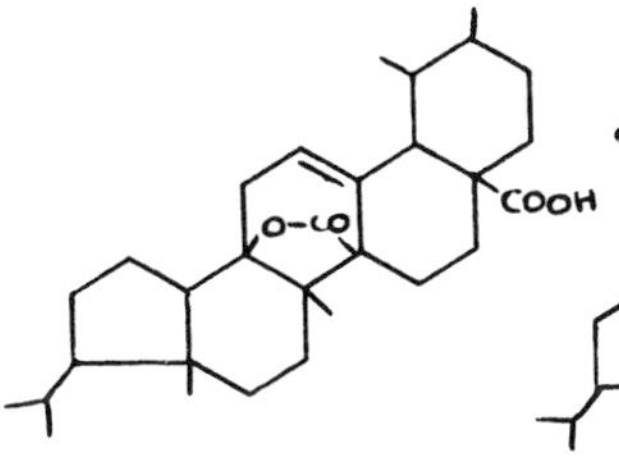

(LXXXIXa)

or

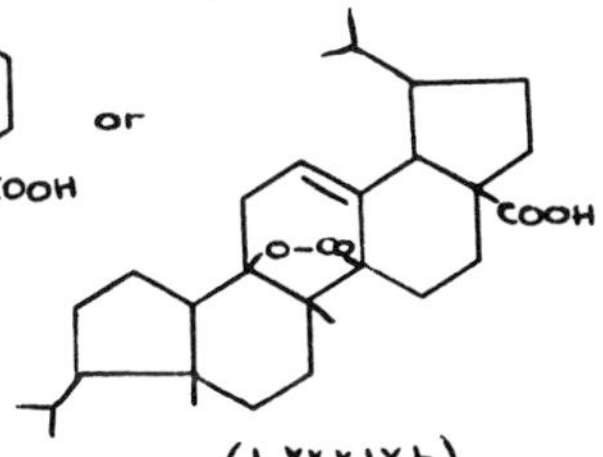

(LXXXIXb)

with α-amyrin (LXXXIX). The derivative (XC) of this on pyrolysis and dehydrogenation gives (XCI) *without* ring expansion. It is believed that further evidence to be described, particularly the reversed Diels-Alder of a derivative (page 164), renders (LXXXVIII), (LXXXIXb), and (XCb) improbable.

In the degradation of α-amyrin described it will be noted, bearing in mind dehydrogenation evidence, that 29 of the carbon atoms out of the original 30 are accounted for in the products. The atom lost is that attached to C_{17}. The position of this and also further proof of the nature of ring E are provided by the sequence of reactions to be described.

By the bromination-dehydrobromination of the 12-ketone derived from α-amyrin, *iso*-α-amyrenonyl acetate may be obtained (XCII). Oxidation of this with selenium dioxide under vigorous conditions gives *iso*-α-amyradienonyl acetate (XCIII), a derivative of *iso*-ursane (XCIV).*

In the formation of (XCIII) a methyl migration takes place (36). This may be initiated by oxidation at C_{13} followed by dehydration and a 1:2 Wagner shift with the ultimate loss of a proton. This process would involve, perhaps, a partial positive charge next to a carbonyl group: (XCII) → (XCIIa) → (XCIIc). By virtue of the isolated double bond (XCIII) gives a strong tetranitromethane colour not given by (XCII). β-Amyrin also gives a similar series of compounds. Now (XCIII) with osmium tetroxide, followed by

*The saturated hydrocarbon based on α-amyrin is known as ursane (cf. oleanane in the β-amyrin series).

(XCa)   OR   (XCb)

(XCI)

MeMgI; -H₂O;
Pd-C

(XCII)   (XCIII)   (XCIV)

(XCII) →   (xciia)   (xciib)   (xciic)

cleavage with lead tetraacetate (37), gave (XCV) ($\lambda_{max.}$ 237 mμ). This could be oxidised (KMnO$_4$) to the corresponding acid (XCVI). Pyrolysis of this acid in vacuo at 290° gave a mixture of products. The higher boiling fraction was partly soluble in alkali and this acidic fraction was methylated with diazomethane to give two isomeric methyl ethers (XCVII) ($\lambda_{max.}$ 246 mμ) and (XCVIII) ($\lambda_{max.}$ 331 mμ). Later the acetate (XCIX) of the parent β-diketone was isolated ($\lambda_{max.}$ 318 mμ) and its structure proven by degradation to (C). The methyl ethers were also obtained in a parallel degradation of β-amyrin, and so prove the identity of configuration at C_3, C_5, C_8, and C_{10} in the two series.

From the lower boiling fraction of the pyrolytic cleavage of (XCVI) an acid was obtained. It was a monounsaturated acid with an isolated double bond and an unhindered carboxyl group. The formulation (CI) was proposed and, as might be expected from such a structure, the acid gave on oxidation with chromic acid β-methyl-tricarballylic acid (CII). Although this oxidation fragment does not distinguish between the ring E proposed and the less probable alternative (LXXXVIII), it provides evidence for the location of the missing carbon atom at C_{17}. Ozonolysis (37) of (CI) gave a keto-dicarboxylic acid (CIII) in which the presence of an acetyl group was shown by reaction with hypoiodite supporting (LXXXIV).

The above degradation, though leading to valid conclusions, is long and complex. Recently, in a transformation of the greatest elegance, the Swiss workers have established directly the nature of

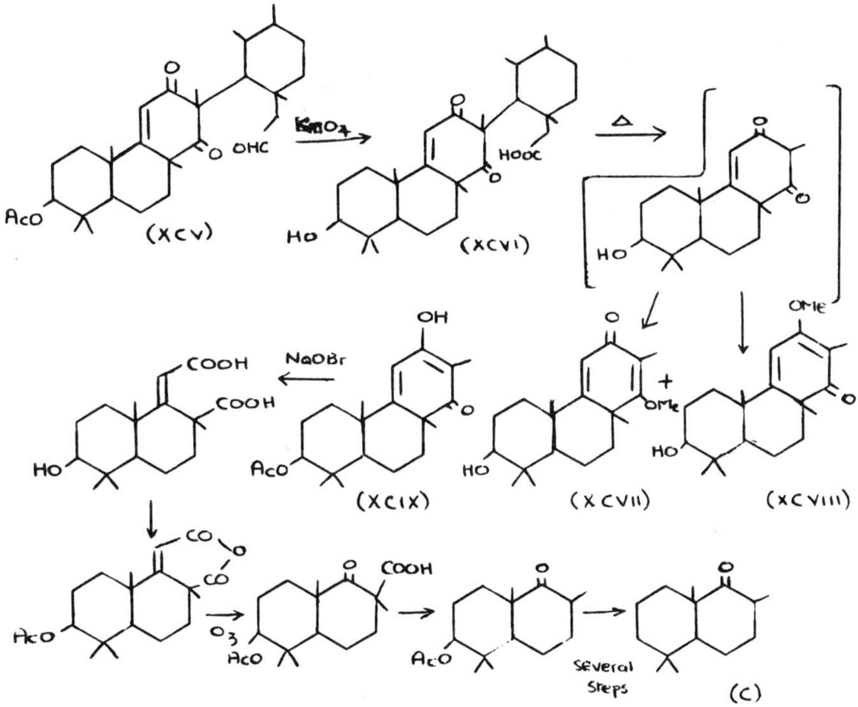

AcO
OHC
(XCV)
HO
HOOC
(XCVI)
Δ
HO
OH
COOH
NaOBr
COOH
HO
AcO
(XCIX)
HO
OMe
+
(XCVII)
OMe
HO
(XCVIII)
AcO
O₃
AcO
COOH
AcO
Several Steps
(C)

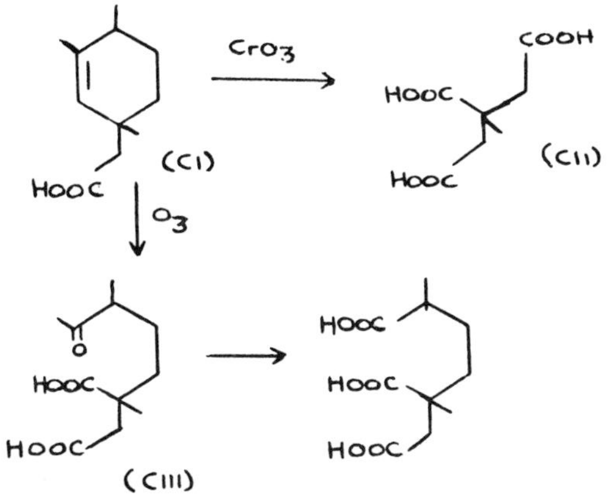

CrO₃
COOH
HOOC
HOOC
(CI)
HOOC
(CII)
O₃
HOOC
HOOC
HOOC
HOOC
HOOC
(CIII)

ring E together with the stereochemistry at C_{20}. Pyrolysis of (XCIII) at $320°$ for a short time resulted in what is probably a reversed Diels-Alder reaction and the separation of ring E. The other fraction (CIVa) was not characterised. This hydrocarbon fragment was epoxidised with monoperphthalic acid and rearranged with boron trifluoride—ether complex to the ketone (CIV). The isolation of the same ketone from D(+)-pulegone (CV) establishes the structure of

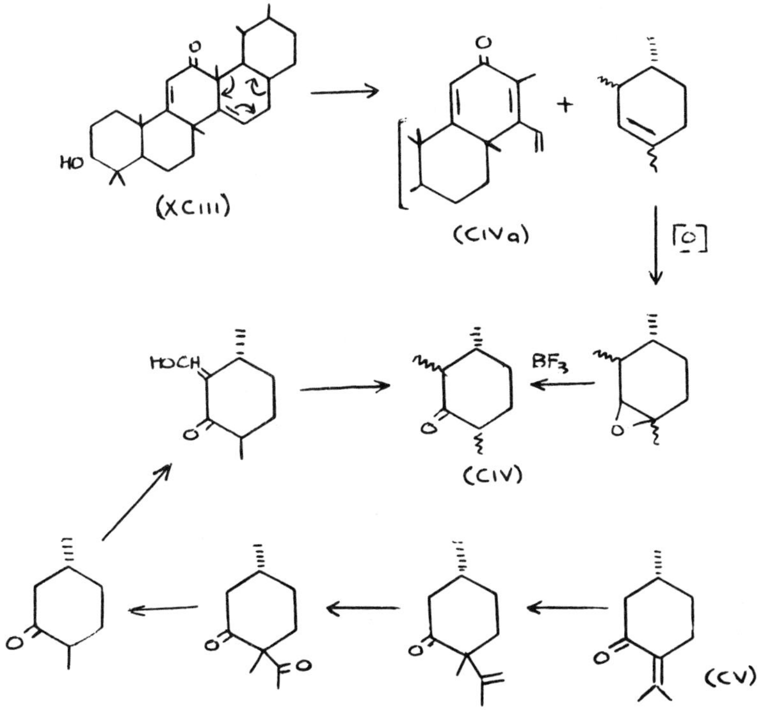

(XCIII)

(CIVa)

[O]

HOCH

(CIV)

BF₃

HOCH

(CV)

(CVI) and, bearing in mind the known absolute configuration of the α-amyrin molecule, also establishes the configuration of the methyl group at C_{20} as α.

This work may be summarised in the stereochemistry implied by (CVI). A major advance is represented by the reactions to be described which were performed by Spring and his collaborators (34). Vigorous treatment of α-amyrin acetate with selenium dioxide gave, in poor yield, (CVII). By hydrogenation (CVIII) was obtained which was isomerised to α-amyrin acetate with acid. The recovery of α-amyrin acetate does not *necessarily* prove that the configuration at C_{18} is the stable one. Since the conversion of α-amyrin acetate into (CVIII) must be very slow, kinetic control in the protonation of (CVIII) may lead to the unstable isomer (60). Finally, with hydrochloric–acetic acid the substance (CVII) is converted into the corresponding β-amyrin derivative (CIX). This complex change is represented here in the simplest carbonium ion terms. Since this transformation does not involve C_9, C_{14}, or C_{17} the expression (CVI) may be expanded, in the knowledge of the stereochemistry of β-amyrin, to (CX). As regards the configuration at C_{18} the following argument has been advanced. Both α-amyrin and β-amyrin, but *not* 18-*iso*-(i.e., 18α-)β-amyrin, undergo rearrangement to the corresponding *iso*dienonyl structure with selenium dioxide; the hydrogen at C_{18} in α-amyrin may thus be as in β-amyrin (i.e., β) (38). Evidence that the configuration at C_{17} and C_{18} is similar in the ursane and oleanane series has also been provided from a comparison (39) of the optical rotations and of stabilities of the lactones of oleanolic and ursolic acid (the 17-carboxyl derivative of α-amyrin). If correct, this permits of the use of the cipher (CXI) as representative of α-amyrin. The final arguments cannot be regarded by any means as rigid, and further confirmation is necessary. In (CXI) the methyl group at C_{19} has been placed in the equatorial conformation for maximum hindrance of the double bond. The reason for the stability of the *cis* junction, if correct, is not yet clear, but may be due to the stabilising effect of the two equatorial methyl substituents. These would become axial if there were epimerisation at C_{18}.

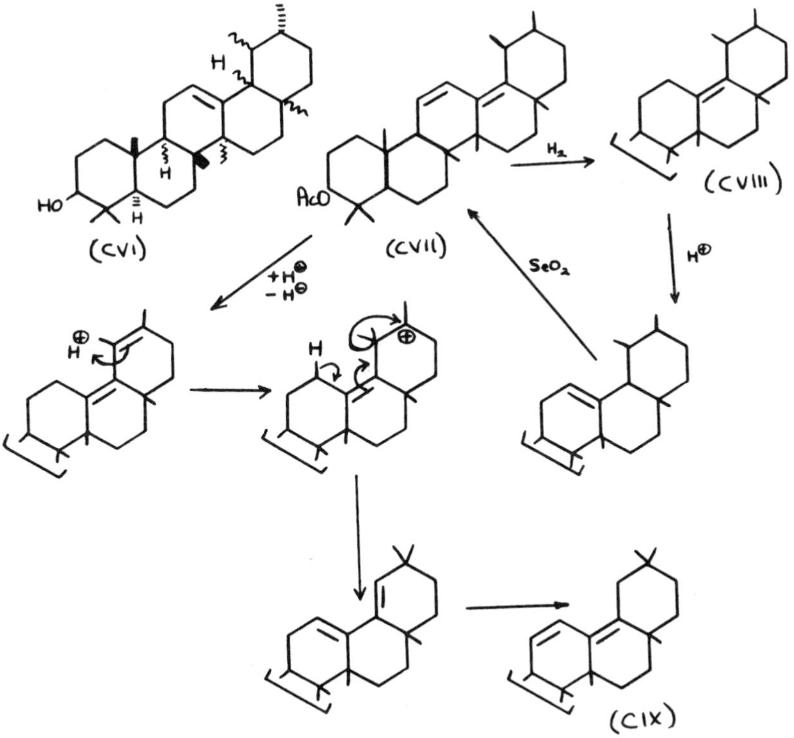

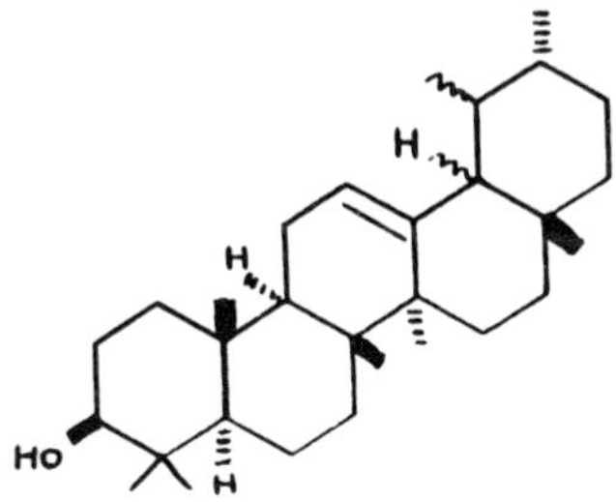

(CX)

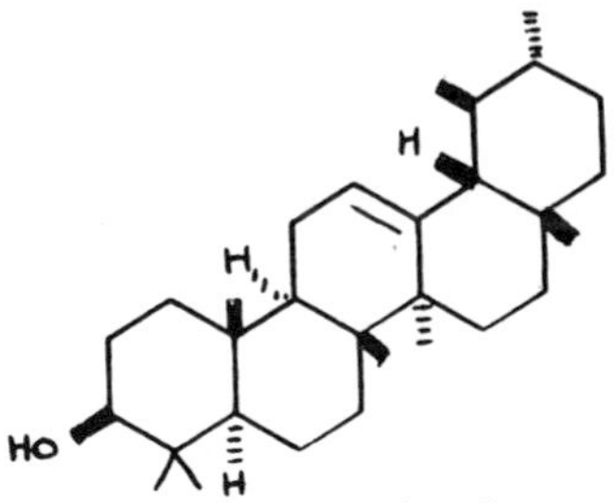

(CXI)

α-Amyrin does not appear to have such a wide variety of naturally occurring derivatives as does β-amyrin. Some of the better known are given in Table 4.

TABLE 4

Naturally Occurring α-Amyrin Derivatives

Compound	Source	Functional Group	Ref.
Asiatic acid	*Hydrocotyle asiatica*	(CXII)	(40)
Brein	Manila elemi resin	3 β-OH 21(22?)-OH	(41)
β-Boswellic acid	Olibanum	3 α-OH 4-COOH	(62)
Phyllanthol	*Phyllanthus engleri* Pax.	(CXIII)	(42)
Quinovic acid	Cinchona bark	(CXIV)	(61)
Ursolic acid	Widely distributed in the wax coating of leaves and fruits	17-COOH	(43)
Uvaol	*Crataegus cuneata*	28-OH	(44)

The saturated alcohol phyllanthol (CXIII) is unusual amongst the amyrin compounds in containing a *cyclo*propane ring. The presence of this feature was shown, simply, by treatment of the acetate with hydrogen chloride–chloroform to give α-amyrin acetate (48).

A number of possible structures could then be written for phyllanthol. Some of these were eliminated in the following way. Using deuterium chloride a deuterated α-amyrin was obtained in which the deuterium atom marked one position of the *cyclo*propane ring terminus. If (CXV) had been correct then the product would have been (CXVI). Oxidation to the unsaturated ketone, however, gave a product in which the deuterium was retained. Another possibility was (CXVII) when the deuterated α-amyrin would be (CXVIII). Conversion to the homoannular diene (CXIX) gave a product in which the deuterium was still retained.

The number of remaining possibilities was considerably narrowed when it was suggested by Cole (49) that, on the basis of a band at 3042–3052 cm⁻¹ in the infra-red, the *cyclo*propane ring of phyllanthol contained a methylene group. The final structure (CXIII) was established (50) when it was shown by quantitative measurements in the 1380 cm⁻¹ region of the infra-red that the deutero-α-amyrin con-

(CXII)

(CXIII)

(CXIV)

(CXV) (CXVI)

(CXVII) (CXVIII) (CXIX)

tained one less methyl group (present, therefore, as —CH$_2$D) than
undeuterated α-amyrin. It will be noted that Markownikoff attack
and axial cleavage of the *cyclo*propane occurs in the conversion to
α-amyrin. The partial synthesis of phyllanthol from an α-amyrin
derivative has recently been accomplished (51). This synthesis
starts from the selenium dioxide product *iso-α*-amyradienonyl acetate (XCIII). With hydrogen chloride this undergoes a remarkable
cyclisation to give (CXX); this is then converted, by standard reactions to phyllanthol acetate.

Phyllanthol has also been prepared from quinovic acid (CXIV).
Reduction of the diacid chloride benzoate with lithium aluminium
hydride gave the triol (CXXI). Treatment of this with methane-
sulphonyl chloride and pyridine gave the dimesylate of a phyllanthol derivative (CXXII), converted by lithium aluminium hydride
and hydrogenation to the diol (CXXIII). Partial hydrolysis of the
diacetate, oxidation, and Wolff-Kishner reduction then gave phyllanthol. This work (52) confirmed the previously established (53,
61) structure of quinovic acid and of uvaol.

THE LUPEOL GROUP

The parent compound of the third important group of triterpenoids
is lupeol. This was first obtained in 1889 from the seeds of *Lupinus
albus*. It has since been isolated from a large number of other
sources and may be the most widely distributed of all triterpenoids.
It is found in at least thirteen families of plants. Instances are
mistletoe, sarsaparilla, Japanese bird-lime, shea-nut fat, and suri-
nam sheet balata. It has the ubiquitous hydroxyl group in ring A,
and also contains an ethylenic linkage. It differs from the amyrins
and their derivatives in that the double bond is easily hydrogenated.
On dehydrogenation 1:2:5-trimethylnaphthalene, 1:5:6-trimethyl-
2-naphthol, and possibly 1:2:5:6-tetramethylnaphthalene were obtained, products which in the amyrins were believed to be derived
from rings A and B. Neither picene nor the naphthalenes sapotalene
(1:2:7-trimethylnaphthalene) and 2:7-dimethylnaphthalene were obtained. These latter hydrocarbons were believed to be formed from

(XCIII, partial)   (CXX)

(CXXI)   (CXXII)

(CXIII)   (CXXIII)

rings D and E of the amyrins, and their absence suggested that lupeol differed from the amyrins in this part of the molecule. The later isolation of formaldehyde as a product of ozonolysis led, eventually, to the proposal (CXXIV) as representing the structure of lupeol (45). The environment of the *iso*propenyl group was shown by oxidation of lupeol acetate with selenium dioxide to (CXXV). Ozonolysis of this to (CXXVI), conversion to the ester, reaction with phenylmagnesium bromide, and dehydration with acetic anhydride gave (CXXVII). Ozonolysis then gave the ketone (CXXVIII) (46).

The key experiment in the elucidation of the structure of lupeol was performed by Ames and Jones (47) and resulted in the rejection of (CXXIV) as an adequate representation of lupeol. Using acid catalysis these authors were able to transform lupenone (CXXIX) into δ-amyrenone (CXXX). This was of known constitution and derived from β-amyrin. This transformation then allowed of the expression (CXXXI) as indicative of the stereochemistry implied for lupeol from that known of β-amyrin and from the general mechanism of the transformation. A compound, betulin (CXXXII), also occurs naturally and differs from lupeol in having a primary alcoholic function at C_{28}. Its relationship to lupeol has been shown by conversion of the 3-monoacetate into the C_{17} aldehyde, and Wolff-Kishner reduction to give that substance. The corresponding acid, betulinic acid, (CXXXIII), also occurs naturally. On treatment with

(CXXIV)   (CXXV)   (CXXVI)   (CXXVII)

(CXXVIII)

(CXXIX)

(CXXX)

(CXXXI)   (CXXXII)   (CXXXIII)

acid, betulonic acid (CXXXIV) was isomerised to a ketolactone (CXXXV). Reduction of this with lithium aluminium hydride followed by acetylation with boron trifluoride-acetic anhydride gave, with concomitant dehydration, moradiol diacetate (CXXXVI). The structure of this substance, derived from morolic acid (LIV), was firmly established. This series of reactions confirms the conclusions expressed in (CXXXI) and, since the centre at C_{13} is not involved in the transformation, requires that in lupeol this should be as in morolic acid—that is, β. (CXXXI) may therefore be expanded to (CXXXVII). This expansion, however, assumes that the lactone (CXXXV) is not formed with a morolic acid derivative as an intermediate. This possibility was excluded when it was shown that under acidic conditions morolic acid gave the 18-*iso*-oleanolic acid lactone.

Further proof of the relationship of lupeol to β-amyrin was provided by Halsall, Jones, and Meakins (54). When a solution of lupeol in ether at 0° was treated with hydrogen chloride a hydrochloride was formed. Whereas silver acetate regenerated the lupeol structure, acetic anhydride gave an isomeric acetate subsequently

(CXXXIV)

(CXXXV)

(CXXXVI)

(CXXXVII)

identified as the acetate of germanicol (CXXXVIII). Now since the
hydrochloride was unaffected by heating with non-ionic solvents
such as xylene, yet in an inert ionising solvent such as benzonitrile
was converted into germanicol, this dehydrochlorination must proceed by a unimolecular solvolysis. The hydrochloride must therefore be (CXXXIX) or (CXL). Reduction of the hydrochloride either
catalytically or with sodium and *iso*propanol gave 18-*iso*-β-amyranol
(CXLI), establishing (CXXXIX) as correct. Since this transformation does not involve C_{18} the hydrogen here, in lupeol, must be presumed the same as in (CXLI); that is α. The configuration of the
chloride atom in (CXXXIX) may be seen to be α from an inspection
of the probable mechanistic path. If it were β (as in CXLII) then
elimination of hydrogen chloride by an SE_2 mechanism (*trans* elimination) should lead to germanicol. Germanicol is, however, obtained only when an SE_1 mechanism prevails, as already mentioned.
With silver acetate, in a reaction presumably initiated by attack of
$Ag^{\oplus}$ on the chloride atom, lupeol is re-formed, and this SN_2-type
reaction will proceed by the path indicated in (CXLIII) wherein the
chloride atom, C_{19}, C_{20}, and C_{21} are coplanar. This requires the
α configuration of the halogen. Also, the mechanism implied in
(CXLIII) requires that the configuration of the *iso*propenyl group in
lupeol be *trans* to the methyl group at C_{17}. The stereochemistry

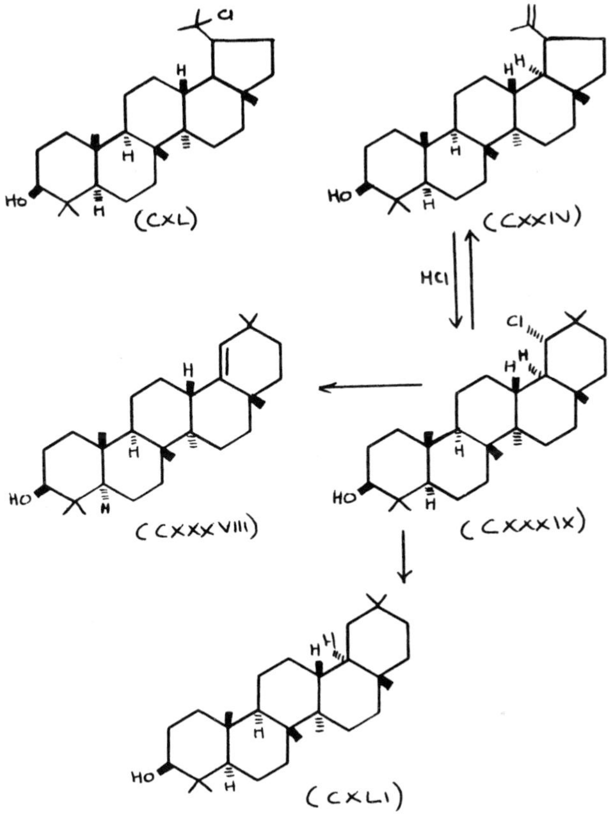

(CXL)

(CXXIV)

HCl

(CXXXVIII)

(CXXXIX)

(CXLI)

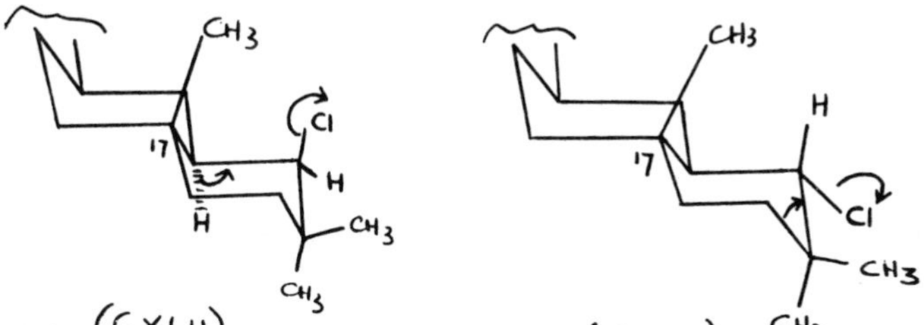

(CXLII)

(CXLIII)

finally arrived at for lupeol therefore is (CXLIV), and this has been confirmed in numerous ways. The production, by the degradation of betulin, of the anhydride (CXLV) originally thought to indicate the β-configuration of the *iso*propenyl group should, if the deductions outlined are correct, involve epimerisation during cyclisation. This was later confirmed (55) when it was shown that the dicarboxylic acid first obtained (CXLVI) did not form an anhydride unless a strong acid, toluene-*p*-sulphonic acid, was used. The dicarboxylic acid (CXLVII) obtained by hydrolysis of this anhydride was not the original one. Two recently discovered cactus triterpenoids, stellatogenin and thurberogenin, are betulinic acid derivatives (57).

Taraxasterol and the related ψ-taraxasterol, whilst not possessing the carbon skeleton of lupeol and its congeners, are probably best considered in relation to this group because of their close chemical similarity. Taraxasterol and ψ-taraxasterol have both been isolated from the roots of the common dandelion and from an extract of artichokes (*Cynara scolymus*). Taraxasterol has also been isolated from a number of other sources under other names, e.g., α-calotropeol (from *Calotropis gigantea*) and giganteol. It has also been found in marguerite flowers, thistle flowers, and in euphorbium resin.

The relationship of taraxasterol to the pentacyclic triterpenoids was established by the following conversions. Hydrogenation of taraxasterol gave a saturated dihydro derivative converted, through the ketone, to the hydrocarbon taraxastane. Betulin on heating with 90% formic acid gave instead of the expected diol diformate the formate of an ether, hydrolysed to an isomer of betulin, *allo*betulin (CXLVIII). The isomer was also formed by the action of other acidic reagents. Its structure was established by oxidation of a derivative with chromic or nitric acid to the lactone (CXXXV). By heating *allo*betulin with benzoyl chloride at 150°, Dischendorfer and Grillmayer obtained a dibenzoate of a diol, heterobetulin. Hydrogenation of the only double bond in this and conversion by standard methods into the hydrocarbon gave heterolupane, identical with taraxastane. The incorporation of ψ-taraxasterol into this group was accomplished when it was shown that it was identical with 28-desoxyheterobetulin (heterolupeol). The complete elucidation of

(CXLIV)   (CXLVI)   (CXLV)   (CXLVII)

(CXLVIII)   (CXLIX)   (CL)

the structures of this interesting group of compounds is due to Jones, Halsall, and their colleagues (56). Taraxasterol contained an *exo*cyclic methylene group. This was shown by successive oxidation with osmium tetroxide and periodic acid to a *nor*ketone, the latter having a band in the infra-red at 1705 cm^{-1} indicative of the presence of the carbonyl group in a six-membered ring. Structures (CXLIX) and (CL) are thus possible for taraxasterol. A distinction in favour of (CL) was made when it was found that both taraxastene and ψ-taraxastene were oxidised to the same $\alpha : \beta$-unsaturated aldehyde (heterolupenal) ($\lambda_{max.}$ 230 mμ). The spectrum of this substance precluded the possibilities of tetrasubstitution of the double bond, requiring therefore that it be represented by (CLI). The possibilities (CLII) and (CLIII) are then available for ψ-taraxasterol. Decision was made here on the basis of spectra which suggested the presence of a triply substituted double bond as in (CLIII). This was confirmed chemically by oxidation to the vicinal diol (CLIV) oxidised to the hydroxy ketone (CLV).

It has already been mentioned that lupenone was isomerised by strong acid to δ-amyrenone. Under somewhat milder conditions an isomer, lupenone-I, is obtained. This is further converted to δ-amyrenone under more vigorous conditions. Oxidation with selenium dioxide gave an isomer of (CLI) having essentially the same ultra-violet spectrum and presumably differing in the configuration at C_{19}. Wolff-Kishner reduction gave, with the expected migration of the double bond (CL). This was then converted to the *nor*ketone, which differed, however, from that obtained from taraxastene derivatives. However, the latter on epimerisation with base gave the same *nor*-ketone as was obtained directly from lupenone-I and so confirmed the isomerisation at C_{19}. The series of reactions also establishes that the methyl group at C_{19} in taraxasterol and ψ-taraxasterol is in the unstable configuration.

Conformational arguments applied here are complex and not compelling. More persuasive evidence was obtained from a consideration of the mechanism of formation of heterobetulin from *allo*-betulin. It seems probable that reaction is initiated by attack on the ethereal oxygen by $C_6H_5CO^{\oplus}$. An SN_2-type displacement at C_{19} should then occur with migration of the C_{20} (axial) α

(CLI)   (CLII)   (CLIII)

(CLV)   (CLIV)

methyl group across the α face of the molecule to the C_{19} α (equatorial) position. If correct this implies that the axial (β) methyl group in lupenone-I is more stable than the equatorial (α) methyl group in taraxasterol and ψ-taraxasterol. The destabilisation is due to interaction with the methylene group at C_{12}. This allocation has been confirmed by a study of molecular rotation. It is of interest that reduction of 18α-oleanan-19-one (CLVI) with sodium and amyl alcohol—a process which should give the thermodynamically more stable product—gives the 19β alcohol—that is, the axial substituent. The structures of taraxasterol, ψ-taraxasterol, and lupenone-I may thus be represented by (CLVII), (CLVIII), and (CLIX). A number of additional facts are available concerning interconversion in this series. Lupeol on boiling with formic acid gives some ψ-taraxasterol. Taraxasteryl acetate may be isomerised by 6% sulphuric acid in acetic acid to lupenyl-I acetate whereas 10% ethanolic sulphuric acid gives ψ-taraxasteryl acetate. The latter with sulphuric acid—acetic acid is converted to the stable lupenyl-I acetate. These numerous interconversions are summarised in the scheme opposite (56). The first stage in all transformations is protonation of the double bond and ring enlargement to give the ion (CLX). This ion is of particular interest and relevance in the context of the recently promulgated biogenetic theory of triterpenoids (page 230). In the presence of an excess of a suitable nucleophile such as chloride ion the ring enlargement is concerted with the stereospecific addition of the anion to give 19α-substituted 18α-oleanane deriva-

(CLVI)

(CLVII)

(CLVIII)

(CLIX)

tives (CLXI). Under more acidic conditions and in the absence of a suitable nucleophile a concerted migration of the α methyl group with the loss of a β proton from C_{21} gives (CLXII), the ψ-taraxasterol system. A complex equilibrium system is set up leading to the formation of the thermodynamically more stable lupene-I system (CLXIII). Only tertiary carbonium ions are involved in this series of changes. The ion (CLXIV) is obtainable by protonation of the taraxasterol system (CLXV) whilst the conversion of lupenone-I derivatives into δ-amyrene products requires the probable conversion of ion (CLXVI) to the ion (CLX). Since (CLXIII) is more stable than (CLXII) the production of (CLXII) may imply insufficient acidity of the medium for the protonation of (CLXII) or else insolubility in a two-phase system thereby displacing equilibrium.

The ion (CLX) may lose a proton to give germanicol derivatives (CLXVII) which may protonate to (CLXVIII) and thence to δ-amyrene derivatives (CLXIX). However, no appreciable amounts of (CLXVII) are found, so that either the conversion of (CLXVII) to (CLXVIII) is very rapid or else, by hydride shift, (CLX) is converted directly to (CLXVIII).

Thus the complex isomerisation and subtleties presented by the acid treatment of lupeol have been resolved, largely by Jones, Halsall, and their colleagues, and interpreted in terms of current carbonium ion theory.

Although the presentation in this chapter has necessitated the division of the common triterpenoids into their original three classes, it will be observed that since conversions from the lupeol series to the β-amyrin, and from the α-amyrin to the β-amyrin have been accomplished such division is without too much significance. A more fruitful view is that expressed more fully (page 228) later, that these substances are examples of the diverse cyclisation-migration processes which include the tetracyclic triterpenoids also. In the following chapter a number of triterpenoids which occur naturally will be discussed which may be considered as being formed in nature by successive rearrangements and migration from the ion (CLX).

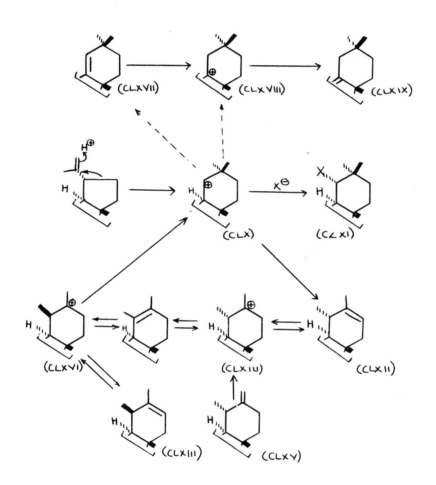

REFERENCES

1. Haworth, R. D., *Ann. Rept. Progr. Chem.*, **34**, 348 (1938).
2. Ruzicka, L., J. Norymberski, and O. Jeger, *Helv. Chim. Acta*, **26**, 2242 (1943).
3. Meyer, A., O. Jeger, V. Prelog, and L. Ruzicka, *Helv. Chim. Acta*, **34**, 747 (1951); Ménard, H., and O. Jeger, *Helv. Chim. Acta*, **36**, 335 (1953).
4. Brownlie, G., M. B. E. Fayez, F. S. Spring, R. Stevenson, and W. S. Strachan, *J. Chem. Soc.*, **1956**, 1377.
5. (a) Ruzicka, L., and K. Hofmann, *Helv. Chim. Acta*, **19**, 114 (1936); Ruzicka, L., F. Ch. Van der Sluys-Veer, and S. L. Cohen, *Helv. Chim. Acta*, **22**, 350 (1939); Ruzicka, L., F. Ch. Van der Sluys-Veer, and O. Jeger, *Helv. Chim. Acta*, **26**, 280 (1943). (b) Gutmann, H., O. Jeger, and L. Ruzicka, *Helv. Chim. Acta*, **33**, 937 (1950). (c) Ruzicka, L., O. Jeger, and M. Winter, *Helv. Chim. Acta*, **26**, 265 (1943).
6. Ruzicka, L., and O. Jeger, *Helv. Chim. Acta*, **24**, 1236 (1941); Beaton, J. M., J. D. Johnston, L. C. McKean, and F. S. Spring, *J. Chem. Soc.*, **1953**, 3660.
7. Barton, D. H. R., N. J. Holness, K. H. Overton, and W. J. Rosenfelder, *J. Chem. Soc.*, **1952**, 3751.
8. Barton, D. H. R., and C. J. W. Brooks, *J. Chem. Soc.*, **1951**, 257.
9. Johnson, W. S., *Experientia*, **7**, 315 (1951).
10. Barton, D. H. R., C. J. W. Brooks, and N. J. Holness, *J. Chem. Soc.*, **1951.** 278.
11. Klyne, W., *J. Chem. Soc.*, **1952**, 2916.
12. Abd El Rahim, A. M., and C. H. Carlisle, *Chem. & Ind. London*, **1954**, 279.
13. King, F. E., T. J. King, and J. M. Ross, *J. Chem. Soc.*, **1955**, 1333.
14. Anantaraman, R., and K. S. M. Pillai, *J. Chem. Soc.*, **1956**, 4369.
15. Ruzicka, L., and W. Wirz, *Helv. Chim. Acta*, **24**, 248 (1941).
16. Bergsteinsson, I., and C. R. Noller, *J. Am. Chem. Soc.*, **56**, 1403 (1934).
17. Zimmermann, J. *Rec. trav. chim.*, **51**, 1200 (1932).
18. Margot, A., and T. Reichstein, *Pharm. Acta Helv.*, **17**, 113 (1942).
19. Simpson, J. C. E., *J. Chem. Soc.*, **1944**, 283.
20. Djerassi, C., and C. M. Foltz, *J. Am. Chem. Soc.*, **76**, 4085 (1954).
21. Kon, G. A. R., and H. R. Soper, *J. Chem. Soc.*, **1940**, 617.
22. Winstersteiner, A., and G. Stein, *Z. physiol. Chem.*, **211**, 5 (1932).
23. Barton, D. H. R., and P. de Mayo, *J. Chem. Soc.*, **1954**, 887.
24. Barton, D. H. R., P. de Mayo, E. W. Warnhoff, O. Jeger, and G. W. Perold, *J. Chem. Soc.*, **1954**, 3689.
25. Morice, I. M., and J. C. E. Simpson, *J. Chem. Soc.*, **1942**, 198.

26. Elliott, D. F., and G. A. R. Kon, *J. Chem. Soc.*, **1939**, 1130.
27. Barton, D. H. R., and P. de Mayo, *J. Chem. Soc.*, **1954**, 900; Barton, D. H. R., P. de Mayo, and J. C. Orr, *J. Chem. Soc.*, **1956**, 4160.
28. Bilham, P., G. A. R. Kon, and W. C. J. Ross, *J. Chem. Soc.*, **1942**, 540; Ruzicka, L., A. Grob, R. Egli, and O. Jeger, *Helv. Chim. Acta*, **26**, 1218 (1943); cf. ref. 59.
29. King, F. E., and T. J. King, *J. Chem. Soc.*, **1956**, 4469.
30. Djerassi, C., L. E. Geller, and A. J. Lemin, *J. Am. Chem. Soc.*, **76**, 4089 (1954); Djerassi, C. and A. E. Lippman, *J. Am. Chem. Soc.*, **77**, 1825 (1955); Djerassi, C., G. H. Thomas, and H. Monsimer, *J. Am. Chem. Soc.*, **77**, 3579 (1955); Djerassi, C., J. A. Henry, A. J. Lemin, T. Rios, and G. H. Thomas, *J. Am. Chem. Soc.*, **78**, 3783 (1956); Djerassi, C., C. H. Robinson, and D. B. Thomas, *J. Am. Chem. Soc.*, **78**, 5685 (1956).
31. McKean, L. C., and F. S. Spring, *J. Chem. Soc.*, **1954**, 1989.
32. Woodward, R. B., quoted by P. Yates and G. H. Stout, *J. Am. Chem. Soc.*, **76**, 5112 (1954).
33. Meisels, A., O. Jeger, and L. Ruzicka, *Helv. Chim. Acta*, **32**, 1075 (1949).
34. Beaton, J. M., F. S. Spring, R. Stevenson, and W. S. Strachan, *J. Chem. Soc.*, **1955**, 2610.
35. Ruzicka, L., and G. Anner, *Helv. Chim. Acta*, **26**, 129 (1943); cf. ref. 53.
36. Ruzicka, L., R. Ruegg, E. Volli, and O. Jeger, *Helv. Chim. Acta*, **30**, 140 (1947); Meisels, A., O. Jeger, and L. Ruzicka, *Helv. Chim. Acta*, **33**, 700 (1950).
37. Ruegg, R., J. Dreiding, O. Jeger, and L. Ruzicka, *Helv. Chim. Acta*, **33**, 889 (1950); Meisels, A., R. Ruegg, O. Jeger, and L. Ruzicka, *Helv. Chim. Acta*, **38**, 1298 (1955).
38. Allan, G. G., and F. S. Spring, *J. Chem. Soc.*, **1955**, 2125.
39. Corey, E. J., and J. J. Ursprung, *J. Am. Chem. Soc.*, **78**, 183 (1956).
40. Polonsky, J., *Bull. soc. chim. France*, **1953**, 173.
41. Buchi, G., O. Jeger, and L. Ruzicka, *Helv. Chim. Acta*, **29**, 442 (1946); Buchi, G., O. Jeger, and L. Ruzicka, *Helv. Chim. Acta*, **31**, 139 (1948); cf. Klyne, W., and W. M. Stokes, *J. Chem. Soc.*, **1954**, 1979.
42. Alberman, K. B., and F. B. Kipping, *J. Chem. Soc.*, **1951**, 2296.
43. Dreiding, J., O. Jeger, and L. Ruzicka, *Helv. Chim. Acta*, **33**, 1325 (1950); cf. Goodson, J. A., *J. Chem. Soc.*, **1938**, 999.
44. Orr, J. E., L. M. Parks, F. W. Dunker, and H. H. Uhl, *J. Am. Pharm. Assoc., Sci. Ed.*, **34**, 39 (1945).
45. Ruzicka, L., and E. Rey, *Helv. Chim. Acta*, **26**, 2143 (1943).
46. Ruzicka, L., W. Huber, and O. Jeger, *Helv. Chim. Acta*, **28**, 195 (1945); Davy, G. S., E. R. H. Jones, and T. G. Halsall, *Rec. trav. chim.*, **69**, 368 (1950).

47. Ames, T. R., T. G. Halsall, and E. R. H. Jones, *J. Chem. Soc.*, **1951**, 450.
48. Barton, D. H. R., and P. de Mayo, *J. Chem. Soc.*, **1953**, 2178.
49. Cole, A. R. H., *J. Chem. Soc.*, **1954**, 3807, 3810.
50. Barton, D. H. R., J. E. Page, and E. W. Warnhoff, *J. Chem. Soc.*, **1954**, 2715.
51. Beaton, J. M., J. D. Easton, M. M. Macarthur, F. S. Spring and R. Stevenson, *J. Chem. Soc.*, **1955**, 3992.
52. Zurcher, A., O. Jeger, and L. Ruzicka, *Helv. Chim. Acta*, **37**, 2145 (1954).
53. Brossi, A., B. Bischof, O. Jeger, and L. Ruzicka, *Helv. Chim. Acta*, **34**, 244 (1951).
54. Halsall, T. G., E. R. H. Jones, and G. D. Meakins, *J. Chem. Soc.*, **1952**, 2862.
55. Guilder, J. M., T. G. Halsall, and E. R. H. Jones, *J. Chem. Soc.*, **1953**, 3024.
56. Halsall, T. G., E. R. H. Jones, and R. E. H. Swayne, *J. Chem. Soc.*, **1954**, 1902, 1905.
57. Djerassi, C., and R. Hodge, *J. Am. Chem. Soc.*, **78**, 3534 (1956).
58. Arya, O. P., and R. C. Cookson, *J. Chem. Soc.*, **1957**, 972.
59. Barton, D. H. R., and N. J. Holness, *J. Chem. Soc.*, **1952**, 78.
60. Zimmermann, H. E., and H. J. Giallombardo, *J. Am. Chem. Soc.*, **78**, 6259 (1956).
61. Barton, D. H. R., and P. de Mayo, *J. Chem. Soc.*, **1953**, 3111.
62. Beton, J. L., T. G. Halsall, and E. R. H. Jones, *J. Chem. Soc.*, **1956**, 2904.

CHAPTER 4

THE TRITERPENOIDS: III

Apart from the main triterpenoid families already discussed there exist, at present, three further naturally occurring pentacyclic triterpenoids which, whilst not having skeletons directly based upon these, are nevertheless closely related. They have, in addition to their considerable chemical interest, a significance because of their position in a postulated general biogenetic pattern.

TARAXEROL

The alcohol alnulin was first isolated from the bark of the grey alder in 1923. An alcohol named taraxerol was isolated from dandelion root in 1938 and, later, from the bark of *Litsea dealbata.* These were shown to be identical in 1950 by Jeger and his colleagues (1). In 1941 Takeda isolated an alcohol, skimmiol, from certain *Skimmia* species and later suggested that it might be identical with taraxerol; this was confirmed by Brooks (2) in 1953. These alternative names have now been discarded and taraxerol, only, retained. The related ketone taraxerone occurs in the bark of the black alder (*Alnus glutinosa*) together with taraxerol.

The investigation of Takeda and his collaborators may be summarised as follows (4). Taraxerol is oxidised to the ketone taraxerone, which is reduced back to the original alcohol with sodium and *iso*amyl alcohol. On selenium dehydrogenation 1:2:3:4-tetramethylbenzene, 2:7-dimethyl-, 1:2:7-trimethyl-, and 1:2:5:6-tetramethylnaphthalene were isolated. 1:8-Dimethylpicene was also obtained, and this suggested a general relationship to the

amyrins. The presence of the $1:2:5:6$-tetramethylnaphthalene was also an indication of the normal triterpenoid rings A and B (see page 130).

Although taraxerol could not be hydrogenated easily the presence of a double bond was shown by conversion of the unsaturated acetate to an epoxide with perbenzoic acid. In cyclohexane–glacial acetic acid in the presence of platinum oxide Takeda claimed to have hydrogenated taraxerol to dihydrotaraxerol. The environment of the hydroxyl group in taraxerol was shown in part by the reactions opposite.

Results of importance were obtained in the following way. Pyrolysis of taraxeryl benzoate at 340° gave, amongst other products, a small amount of a doubly unsaturated hydrocarbon. This on hydrogenation, with the saturation of one of the ethylenic linkages, was converted to δ-amyrene (I) (olean-13(18)-ene). The same hydrocarbon was obtained by the Clemmensen reduction of taraxerone. From this and other work Takeda was led to the conclusion, reasonable at that time, that taraxerol was olean-18-en-3β-ol (II). This proposal was invalidated later (5) when this structure was assigned to germanicol.

The investigations of the Swiss workers confirmed much of the earlier work, but through awareness of the powerful acidic potentialities of Clemmensen conditions they did not accept that an oleanane skeleton was necessarily implied by Takeda's work.

The next, and a major, advance in taraxerol chemistry, was made when it was discovered by Brooks (2) that oxidation of taraxeryl acetate with selenium dioxide gave two isolable products which he identified. These were oleana-11:13(18)-dienyl acetate (III) and the dienedione (IV). These results establish decisively the presence of the hydroxyl group at C_3 despite previous allegations that the corresponding carbonyl group could not be removed by normal Wolff-Kishner reduction (1), although this is a property expected of C_3 ketones. Now with the clearly made proviso that no skeletal change had taken place during the selenium dioxide oxidation the structure (V) was proposed for taraxerol after elimination of already assigned structures. In doing so, it was recognised that the double

(II)

(I)

(III)

(V)

(IV)

bond was trisubstituted, as supported by the presence of a band at 814 cm^{-1} in the infra-red.

The assumption that no rearrangement takes place when taraxeryl acetate is submitted to the action of selenium dioxide was soon questioned. The grounds for doubt, as expressed by Spring and his collaborators, were as follows. If (V) were indeed correct then the oxide derived from it must be (VI). This oxide was shown by Takeda to rearrange under the influence of mineral acid to an unsaturated alcohol. This must be represented, on the basis of (V), as (VII) (the derived unsaturated ketone would then be (VIII)). But (VII) is an allylic alcohol and as such would be unlikely to survive the conditions of its genesis. A further objection raised was that the formation of a small amount of oleana-2 : 12-diene on dry distillation of taraxeryl benzoate, as reported by Takeda, would require the migration of the double bond at 18 : 19 past the thermodynamically more stable 13(18) position to the less stable 12 : 13 position leaving, also, the less stable configuration at C_{18}.

An extension of the latter argument also applied to the Clemmensen reduction of taraxerone. After 24 hours of such treatment olean-13(18)-ene was isolated, but after 8 hours the Swiss workers (1) isolated a hydrocarbon the constants of which were recognised by Spring and his colleagues as resembling a mixture of olean-12-ene and olean-13(18)-ene. If correct, this required on the basis of (V) that the intermediate (13)18-unsaturated hydrocarbon be converted to olean-12-ene rapidly, and then back slowly. The correctness of the original facts was clearly demonstrated when a suspension of taraxeryl acetate in acetic acid at $90°$ was treated with hydrochloric acid. In a very short time an excellent yield of β-amyrin acetate was obtained.

These results were strongly indicative that, in the formation of oleanane derivatives from taraxerol, a rearrangement had taken place. The sole remaining possibility not involving a rearrangement was (IX).

The likelihood of such a transformation seems small, because it requires non-Markownikoff addition of a proton to the double bond. A clear decision was possible by examination of the unsaturated ketone derived from the epoxide. This was found *not* to be a con-

(VI)   (VII)   (VIII)

(IX)   (X)

jugated ketone thereby indicating that a rearrangement had taken place in the opening of the oxide. Dehydration of the related unsaturated alcohol with phosphorus oxychloride and pyridine gave a non-conjugated dienyl acetate and this on hydrogenation gave β-amyrin acetate. Clearly, since rearrangement has led to the β-amyrin structure taraxerol cannot already possess it. Two possibilities, at least, then presented themselves, (X) and (XI). The conversion of (X) to β-amyrin could be viewed as protonation of the double bond with concerted methyl migrations from C_{14} and C_{13} as represented. This is strongly reminiscent of the euphenol → iso-euphenol rearrangement (6) (page 100). A similar rearrangement for (XI) is also possible. The formulation (XI) was preferred because of certain analogies with previous work in the β-amyrin series (7). Thus, as previously mentioned, both the amyrins may be converted into substances having the partial structure (XII). Oxidation with selenium dioxide then gives (XIII). By Wolff-Kishner reduction of (XIII) in the β-amyrin series two unconjugated dienes (XIV) and (XV) were obtained. On treatment with mineral acid (XIV) is converted to the homoannular diene (XVI). Under similar conditions (XV) is converted into (XVII). Under very vigorous and prolonged acid treatment (XVI) may be converted to (XVII). These rearrangements, with attendant methyl migrations, bore a remarkable resemblance to the conversion of taraxerol to β-amyrin. An even more striking parallel was the oxidation, with attendant rearrangement, of (XIV) by selenium dioxide to the conjugated dienedione (XVIII) by the action of selenium dioxide.

(XI)

(XII)   (XIII)

(XVIII)   (XIV)   (XV)

(XVI)   (XVII)

These analogies stimulated Spring and his colleagues to attempt the partial synthesis of (XI). This was achieved as shown in (XIII) → (XI). The reduction of the conjugated double bond was carried out with lithium and liquid ammonia. The removal of the carbonyl group required a forcing variant of the Wolff-Kishner reduction (8). The product was taraxerol.

With the structure of taraxerol established, the derived oxide may then be formulated as (XIX) and the unsaturated alcohol as (XX). The related ketone, on reduction with lithium aluminum hydride, gave a different isomeric alcohol. This new alcohol was chemically more hindered than the original one, as shown by the fact that whilst acetylation of (XX) under normal conditions gave a 3 : 15-diacetate, that of (XXI) gave only a monoacetate. This suggested that the hydroxyl group in the original alcohol (XX) was equatorial, that is α, in orientation; the oxide must be similarly oriented. The rearrangement which occurs on oxide opening is presumably not concerted with it since the migrating methyl group is on the same side of the molecule as the oxide. The formation of a *trans* glycol intermediate is not impossible, in which case the migration could be concerted with the loss of the $C_{14} \beta$ hydroxyl group.

Taraxerol, while of intrinsic chemical interest, has a place also in a pattern of biogenesis which is becoming clearer as the structures of more triterpenoids are unravelled. In the general concept of the genesis of the triterpenoids an ion (or equivalent) (XXII) which is of importance has already been mentioned (page 182). Now by hydride shift—specifically a 1 : 2 shift in which stereochemistry is retained—this may be converted to (XXIII), and again to (XXIV). Now loss of a proton leads to the β-amyrin series whereas migration of the methyl group at C_{14} gives (XXVI) which leads to taraxerol (XXV). Since these transformations are in part not reproducible in the laboratory they might, at least as far as accommodating taraxerol, be regarded as not compelling. However, further stages in the "spinal" rearrangement have very recently been uncovered.

(XIII)   (XI)

(XIX)   (XX)

(XXI)

(XXII)   (XXIII)   (XXIV)
                                        -H⊕

1:2 shift

(XXV)   (XXVI)

ALNUSENONE (GLUTINONE)

In 1953 Chapon and David isolated from the bark of the black alder a new triterpenoid unsaturated ketone which they named glutinone (10). Spring and his colleagues, independently, isolated from the same source a triterpenoid which they named alnusenone. The compounds proved to be identical and, though it is not clear yet which name has preference, the name alnusenone will be used here for convenience and without commitment. The structure of this interesting substance has very recently been elucidated by the British workers, and the work described below is largely to be attributed to them (9).

The carbonyl group in alnusenone is unhindered, as shown by the formation of an oxime; it is also unconjugated. Further, reduction of the ketone with either sodium and alcohol or with lithium aluminium hydride gives the same alcohol, and this is readily acylated. The double bond, also, is not hindered, and alnusenyl acetate may be readily hydrogenated to the saturated alnusanyl acetate. From a study of spectra the double bond was presumed to be trisubstituted. Some confusion exists as to the reaction of alnusenyl acetate with osmium tetroxide, but it appears most probable that the evidence provided by Spring and his colleagues is correct. These authors assert that a triol is obtained, which after conversion to a diacetate is stable to chromic acid.

Reduction of alnusenone by the Wolff-Kishner technique gave the hydrocarbon alnusene (XXVII). The key experiment in this structural investigation was the treatment of this hydrocarbon with hydrochloric and acetic acid mixture. The product, by an extraordinary series of shifts, was the hydrocarbon β-amyrene-III (δ-amyrene) (XXVIII) now recognised to contain also some (XXIX), 18 α-olean-12-ene. These transformations are expressed as shown. The same series of reactions could not, however, be performed on the original ketone now to be formulated as (XXX). Mild acid treatment gave an isomer alnus-5(10)-enone (XXXI).

Oxidation of alnusenyl acetate with selenium dioxide gave alnusadienyl acetate (10) (XXXII) which can be hydrogenated back to the original acetate, thus precluding the possibility of rearrange-

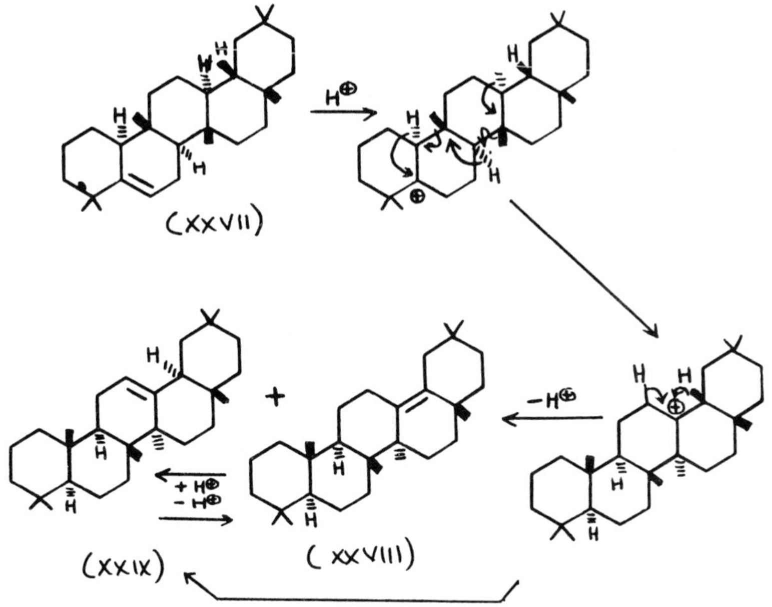

(XXVII)

(XXIX)   +   (XXVIII)

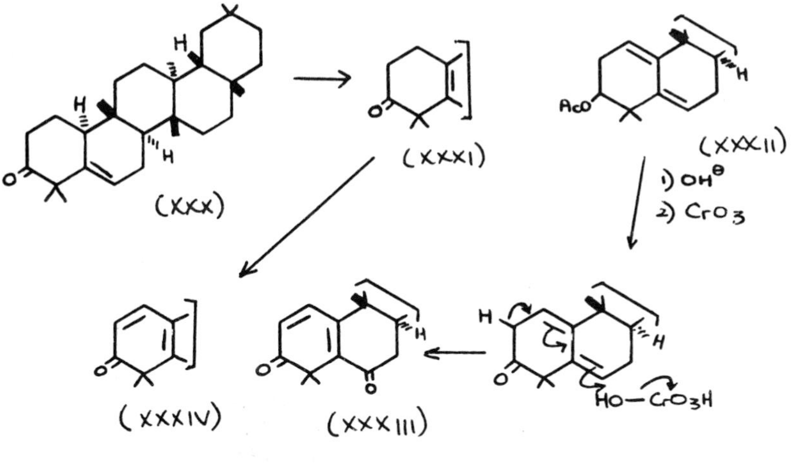

(XXX)   (XXXI)   (XXXII)

1) OH$^{\ominus}$
2) CrO$_3$

(XXXIV)   (XXXIII)

ment. The spectrum of (XXXII) indicated a heteroannular diene; oxidation of the derived alcohol with chromic acid, proceeding probably by the indicated mechanism, then gave the dienedione (XXXIII). This provides powerful evidence for the environment of the carbonyl group and double bond. Further evidence is provided by the conversion of (XXXI) to (XXXIV) by bromination-dehydrobromination ($\lambda\lambda_{max.}$ 207, 322 mμ). Whilst this evidence is, together with the conversion to compounds of the β-amyrin group, very persuasive in itself, with the possible exception of the configuration at C_{18}, the structure of alnusenol has been clearly demonstrated by partial synthesis from another triterpenoid, friedelin. This substance, the structure of which will be described below, gives a bromo derivative (XXXV). Treatment of this with silver acetate gives a mixture of (XXXI) and (XXX). The mixture was reduced to the alcohols with lithium aluminium hydride and separated as the acetates.

The position of alnusenone in the biogenetic pattern is clear. The ion (XXVI) by further 1 : 2 stereospecific shifts as those postulated to lead to taraxerol passes through (XXXVI), (XXXVII), (XXXVIII), and (XXXIX). The latter then loses a proton. This extraordinary postulated series of migrations across the main perhydropicene skeleton is made more convincing by the nature of the ultimate transformation compound friedelin.

FRIEDELIN AND CERIN

Cork is a readily available material, and it is not surprising that the first attempts to isolate any organic constituents were made as early as 1807 by Chevreul. He obtained from it a wax which he called "cérine," but the unhomogeneity of this was shown later by Istate and Ostrogovich who isolated from it two crystalline substances now recognised as the triterpenoids friedelin and cerin.

The first detailed investigations of friedelin were made by Drake and his colleagues in the period 1936–1940 (11). They established securely that it was a ketone of the formula $C_{30}H_{50}O$ and, since no colour was given with tetranitromethane and there was no conjugation with the ketone, they concluded that there was no double bond

(XXXV) → (XXXI)

(XXX)

(XXVI) → (XXXVI) → (XXXVII)

(XXX) ← [O] ← (XXXIX) ← (XXXVIII)

and that it contained a saturated pentacyclic system. On Clemmensen reduction of friedelin the hydrocarbon friedelane was obtained. Sodium and amyl alcohol reduction gave the secondary alcohol friedelanol.

So far the only evidence adduced for the triterpenoid nature of the substance was the analysis. Evidence was now provided. From selenium dehydrogenation experiments on friedelanol there were obtained 1:2:5-, and 1:2:7-trimethylnaphthalenes, 1:2:5:6-tetramethylnaphthalene, 1:2:8-trimethylphenanthrene (XL), and, of particular importance, 1:8-dimethylpicene (XLI). This latter, also obtained from the amyrins, strongly suggests a perhydropicene nucleus.

Apart from this important contribution, Drake and his colleagues made other interesting degradative investigations of the friedelin molecule. Pyrolysis of friedelanyl benzoate, with the elimination of benzoic acid, gave friedelene oxidised to the $\alpha:\beta$-unsaturated ketone friedelenone. Oxidation of friedelin with chromic acid gave two substances. The main product was a keto acid, friedelonic acid, formed without the loss of carbon atoms; the other was a dicarboxylic acid with one carbon atom less. This transformation requires the grouping

$$\underset{\displaystyle }{-\!-CO\!-\!-CH\!-\!-C.}\overset{\textstyle C}{\overset{\textstyle |}{}}$$

It was then found that by heating to 250° friedelonic acid (XLII) lost carbon dioxide to give a hydrocarbon, norfriedelene (XLIII). Since this hydrocarbon was oxidised by potassium permanganate to give *nor*friedelonic acid (XLIV), a keto acid with the same number of carbon atoms, the sequence of reactions may be represented as shown opposite. The partial formula (XLV) therefore follows for friedelin.

The problem was then taken up by Ruzicka, Jeger, and their collaborators (12). These authors found that oxidation of friedelin under somewhat different conditions from those used by Drake gave

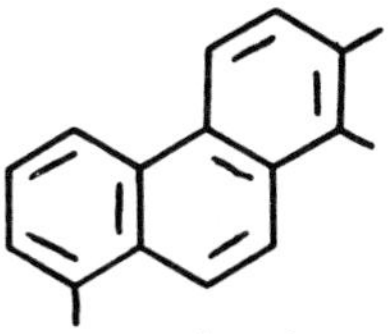

(XL)

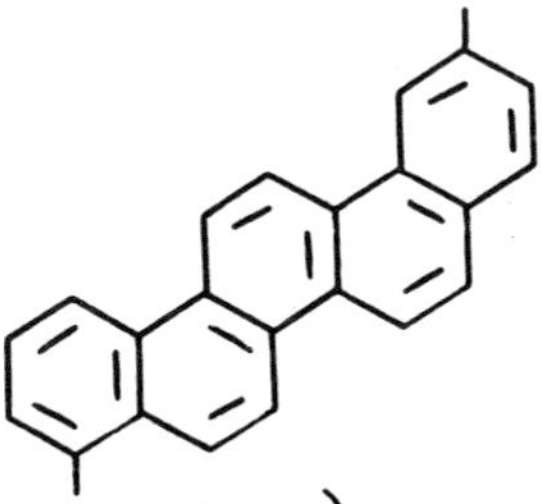

(XLI)

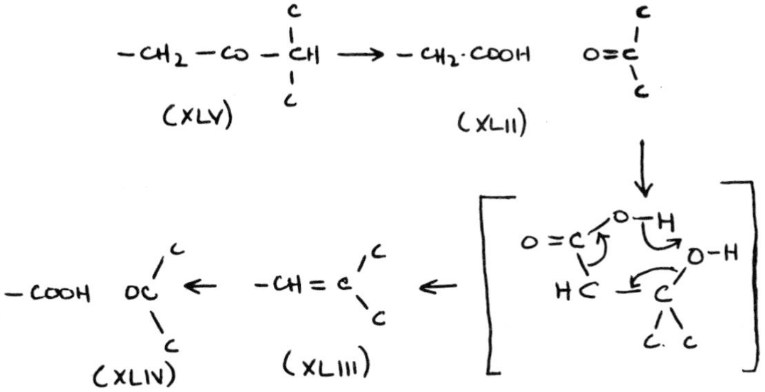

$$-CH_2-CO-\overset{\overset{\textstyle C}{|}}{\underset{\underset{\textstyle C}{|}}{CH}} \longrightarrow -CH_2 \cdot COOH \qquad O=\overset{\overset{\textstyle C}{|}}{\underset{\underset{\textstyle C}{}}{C}}$$

(XLV)   (XLII)

$$-COOH \quad O\overset{C}{\underset{C}{\diagdown}}C \quad \longleftarrow \quad -CH=C\overset{C}{\underset{C}{\diagup}} \quad \longleftarrow \quad \left[O=C\overset{O-H}{\underset{HC}{\diagup}} \overset{C}{\underset{C}{\diagup}} \overset{O-H}{\underset{C \cdot C}{\diagdown}} \right]$$

(XLIV)   (XLIII)

a C_{30} dicarboxylic acid, friedelindicarboxylic acid (XLVI). This could be converted into an anhydride which, on pyrolysis, gave a ketone, norfriedelanone (XLVII). Mild oxidation of this with se-enium dioxide introduced a conjugated double bond and gave nor-friedelenone. No structural rearrangement had taken place here because reduction gave back (XLVII). Further and more vigorous oxidation with selenium dioxide then introduced a further carbonyl group to give a substance originally termed norfriedelenedione. This substance is an α-diketone, because it may be cleaved by hydrogen peroxide to a dicarboxylic acid. The implication, as shown in the sequence opposite, is that there are two methylene groups flanking the carbonyl group on the same side in friedelin. Ozonolysis of the dicarboxylic acid (anhydride) resulted in cleavage of the double bond and formation of a ketone. The adjacent carboxyl group was lost as carbon dioxide (β-keto acid). This formation of a ketone requires that the carbon atom marked with a star in the partial formula of friedelin (XLVIII) bear one hydrogen and no more, as shown.

This ketone had the formula $C_{25}H_{42}O_2$ and was tetracyclic. The subsequent attempts were to fit the partial formula (XLVIII) into the pentacyclic framework suggested by the isolation of the 1,8-dimethylpicene. The problem was, in part, simplified when, contrary to earlier reports, it was shown (14) that the ketocarboxylic acid (XLII) was a methyl ketone. The part formula (XLVIII) was then expanded to (XLIX). But since this represents the terminal ring of a triterpenoid, it is apparent that a methyl group is missing. This implies either some deviation in the presently accepted biogenetic scheme, though perhaps at a late stage, or else a flaw in the evidence adduced. The source of the error was revealed by Spring and his co-workers. It lies in the nature of the selenium dioxide oxidation products. The compound known as norfriedelenedione represented by (L) should be a C_{29} compound. Reinvestigations showed that it had, in fact, only 28 carbon atoms (13,14). If there were no hydrogen at the asterisked carbon atom in (XLIX), then norfriedelenone would have to be represented by (LI). The conversion of (LI) to what must now be termed bisnorfriedelenedione (LII) therefore involves the loss of a methyl group and its replacement by a ketonic

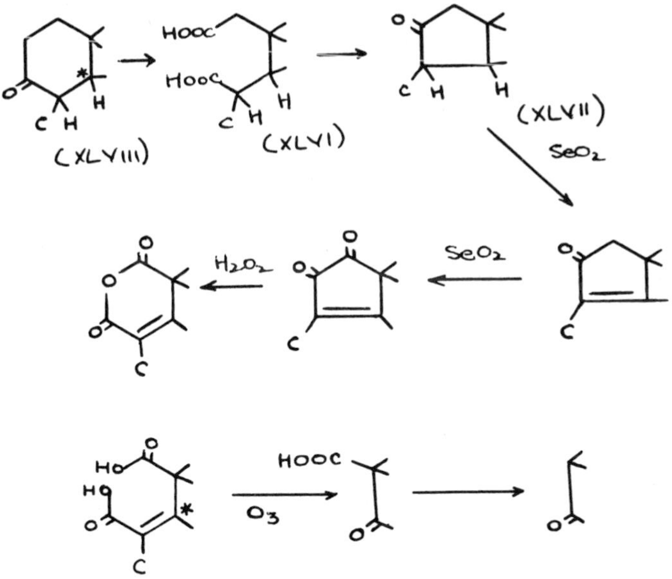
HOOC
HOOC
(XLVIII)
(XLVI)
(XLVII)
SeO₂
SeO₂
H₂O₂
HOOC
O₃

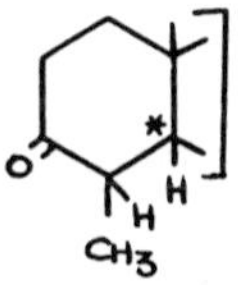
CH₃

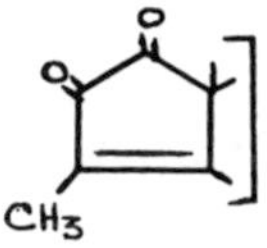
CH₃

(XLIX) (L)

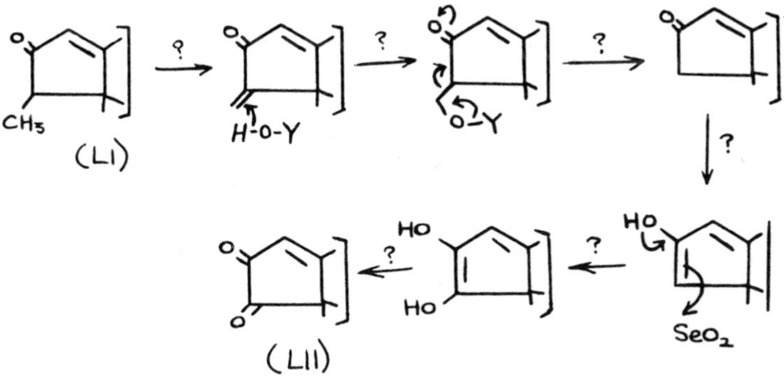
CH₃
(LI)
H-O-Y
O-Y
HO
HO
HO
SeO₂
(LII)

function. The mechanism of this unusual reaction provoked by the vigorous conditions (SeO_2 at $180°$) is not known. The path indicated is merely conjectural. The oxidation process to the dienone is analogous to that suggested (22) for the oxidation of 1:4-diketones to enediones. HOY is intended to imply water or equivalent.

The enedione (LII) is obtainable (12), as was shown by the Swiss workers, by other routes. Conversion of friedelin to the enol benzoate followed by chromic acid oxidation gives, by the introduction of a carbonyl group, the enol benzoate of an α-diketone. Selenium dioxide oxidation of this gives (LII). The terminal ring of friedelin may therefore be written as (LIII).

It was found by the Swiss workers that whilst cleavage of (LII) under mild conditions with hydrogen peroxide gave the anhydride of the dicarboxylic acid, now written as (LIV), more vigorous treatment gave a non-conjugated unsaturated C_{26} acid (LV).

Oxidation of (LV) as the methyl ester introduces a carbonyl group ($\lambda_{max.}$ 247 mμ) (LVI) and hydrolysis then results in decarboxylation of the vinylogous β-keto acid to give (LVII). This may be hydrogenated to the saturated ketone (LVIII) (15). On deuterium bromide–catalysed deuterium exchange three α hydrogens were found to be present.

Further, the C_{25} ketone obtained by the Swiss workers by the ozonolysis of what is now (LIV) exchanged, under similar conditions, *one* α hydrogen and so must be represented by the partial formulae (LIX) (14,15). This allows of the expansion of the partial formula of friedelin to (LX). Since 1,8-dimethylpicene contains twenty-four carbon atoms, the remaining six are probably present as methyl groups. Two of these are incorporated in (LX), leaving four. Two of these may be placed at C_{13} and C_{14} for the following reasons. The production of 1,2,7-trimethylnaphthalene is not possible from the rings represented in (LX); it must therefore represent the dehydrogenation product of the other terminal rings. 1:2:8-Trimethylphenanthrene cannot represent this same section of the molecule and so must include (LX). This is rendered probable because the vicinal methyl groups appear in the same relative place in the

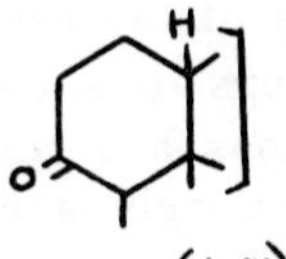

(LIII)

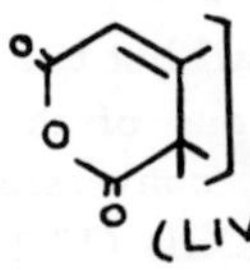

(LIV)

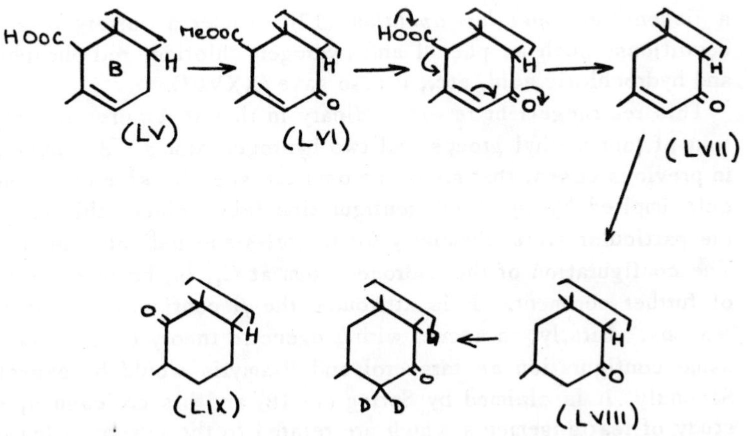

(LV) (LVI) (LVII) (LVIII) (LIX)

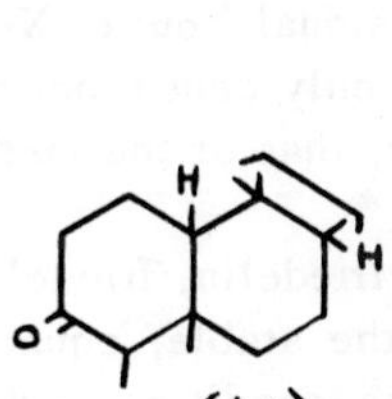

(LX)

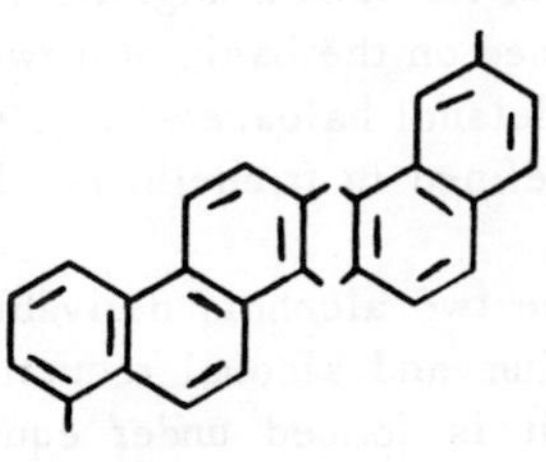

molecule as a whole. This allows of the expansion of (LX) to
(LXI) in which all but two methyl groups are accounted for.

The correctness of these deductions has been directly demonstrated by the conversion, under strongly acidic conditions, of
friedel-3-ene (LXII) (13,16) to olean-13(18)-ene (XXVIII) contami-
nated with the usual equilibrium proportion of 18α-olean-12-ene
(XXIX). A similar transformation has been effected on the alcohol
*epi*friedelanol. This compound is obtained from friedelin by reduction with lithium aluminium hydride and has also been isolated from
a lichen *Ceratopetalum apetalum* (17). Under a variety of acidic
conditions, such as phenol and hydrogen chloride, red phosphorus
and hydrochloric acid, etc., it also gave (XXVIII).

This rearrangement is extraordinary in that it requires the migration of four methyl groups and two hydrogen atoms. Assuming, as
in previous cases, that migration over the specific side of the molecule implied by the final configuration takes place, this requires
the particular stereochemistry for friedel-3-ene indicated in (LXII).
The configuration of the hydrogen atom at C_{18} is, however, needful
of further comment. It is attributed the β configuration for three
reasons. Firstly, in accord with biogenetic theory (see below) the
same configuration as taraxerol and β-amyrin would be expected.
Secondly, it is claimed by Spring (13,18) and his colleagues, in a
study of rearrangements which are related to the essential features
of the present transformation, that a *cis* locking of rings D/E is
essential for such a migration. Finally, the assigned configuration
is claimed on the basis of a two-dimensional Fourier X-ray analysis
on friedelanol haloacetates (19). The only centre not stereochemi-
cally defined in friedelin is, therefore, that of the methyl group at
C_4.

Of the two alcohols derivable from friedelin, friedelanol, formed
by sodium and alcohol reduction, is the stable, equatorial isomer
since it is formed under equilibrating conditions (20). *Epifrie-
delanol*, which is, therefore, axial, is readily dehydrated under
ionic conditions to give (LXII), and a four-centre planar transition
state may be assumed. This requires an axial (α) hydrogen at C_4.
The methyl group is therefore β (equatorial) and friedelin may be
represented by the cipher (LXIII). Other aspects of the stereo-

(LXI)

(LXII)

$(XXVIII) + (XXIX)$

(LXIII)

chemistry have been investigated chemically by Corey and Ursprung, and their findings (15) are in accord with this expression.

It might be thought that the acid-catalysed rearrangement of friedel-3-ene to (XXVIII) and (XXIX) should be a fully concerted process. It has been shown very recently, however (24), that under some conditions at least it is not so. When friedel-3-ene in boiling acetic acid is treated with a stream of hydrogen chloride the compound (LXV) is obtained. This substance, which under more vigorous conditions is transformed to (XXVIII) and (XXIX), has been obtained by Wolff-Kishner reduction of (XXXI) (10). This being so a certain doubt might be attached to the configuration at C_5 and C_{10}; other evidence is available to support that shown in (LXIII) (14,15, 19,23).

Continuing the biogenetic scheme represented on page 182, friedelin represents the ultimate transformation from the original postulated ion (or equivalent) (XXII). This passes to (XXVI) (page 198) which leads to taraxerol and (XXXIX) (page 202), which in turn leads to alnusenone, and finally (XXXIX) may be transformed, again by 1:2 shifts, to (LXIV). By loss of a proton this gives friedelin.

Cerin, the accompanying substance with friedelin in cork, is an α-hydroxy ketone. This is proven by its mild oxidation to an α-diketone and to friedelin dicarboxylic acid, and by its Wolff-Kishner reduction (15) to friedel-2-ene. Similar elimination reactions have been recorded (21). The hydroxyl group may also be eliminated by treatment with zinc and acetic acid to give friedelin, demonstrating that the positions of the carbonyl and hydroxyl are not reversed. From a study of spectra Takahashi and Ourisson (14) conclude that the hydroxyl group is equatorial (α) and that cerin may therefore be represented by (LXV).

A number of other derivatives of friedelin have been isolated recently from the bark of *Siphonodon australe* Benth; their structures have not been elucidated yet (23).

(LXV)

(XXXIX)   (LXIV)   (LXII)

(LXV)

REFERENCES

1. Koller, E., A. Hiestand, P. Dietrich, and O. Jeger, *Helv. Chim. Acta,* **33**, 1050 (1950).
2. Brooks, C. J. W., *J. Chem. Soc.,* **1955,** 1675.
3. Beaton, J. M., F. S. Spring, R. Stevenson, and J. L. Stewart, *J. Chem. Soc.,* **1955,** 2131.
4. Takeda, K., *J. Pharm. Soc. Japan,* **61,** 63 (1941); **62,** 114 (1942); *Chem. Abstr.,* **36,** 444 (1942); **44,** 9384 (1950); **45,** 586, 5696 (1951).
5. Barton, D. H. R., and C. J. W. Brooks, *J. Chem. Soc.,* **1951,** 257.
6. Barton, D. H. R., J. F. McGhie, M. K. Pradhan, and S. A. Knight, *J. Chem. Soc.,* **1955,** 876.
7. Allan, G. G., J. D. Johnston, and F. S. Spring, *J. Chem. Soc.,* **1954,** 1546.
8. Barton, D. H. R., D. A. J. Ives, and B. R. Thomas, *J. Chem. Soc.,* **1955,** 2056.
9. Beaton, J. M., F. S. Spring, and R. Stevenson, *J. Chem. Soc.,* **1955,** 2616; Spring, F. S., J. M. Beaton, R. Stevenson, and J. L. Stewart, *Chem. & Ind., London,* **1956,** 1054.
10. Chapon, S., and S. David, *Bull. soc. chim., France,* **1953,** 333; Chapon, S., *Bull. soc. chim. France,* **1955,** 1076, 1630.
11. Drake, N. L., and J. K. Wolfe, *J. Am. Chem. Soc.,* **62,** 3018 (1940); and previous papers in this series.
12. Ruzicka, L., O. Jeger, and P. Ringnes, *Helv. Chim. Acta,* **27,** 972 (1944); Perold, G. W., K. Meyerhans, O. Jeger, and L. Ruzicka, *Helv. Chim. Acta,* **32,** 1246 (1949).
13. Brownlie, G., F. S. Spring, R. Stevenson, and W. S. Strachan, *J. Chem. Soc.,* **1956,** 2419.
14. Takahashi, T., and G. Ourisson, *Bull. soc. chim. France,* **1956,** 353.
15. Corey, E. J., and J. J. Ursprung, *J. Am. Chem. Soc.,* **78,** 5041 (1956).
16. Dutler, H., O. Jeger, and L. Ruzicka, *Helv. Chim. Acta,* **38,** 1268 (1955).
17. Bruun, T., *Acta Chem. Scand.,* **8,** 76 (1954); Bruun, T. and P. R. Jefferies, *Acta Chem. Scand.,* **8,** 1948 (1954).
18. Allan, G. G., F. S. Spring, R. Stevenson, and W. S. Strachan, *J. Chem. Soc.,* **1955,** 3371; Fayez, M. B. E., J. Grigor, F. S. Spring, and R. Stevenson, *J. Chem. Soc.,* **1955,** 3378; Shaw, J. I., F. S. Spring, and R. Stevenson, *J. Chem. Soc.,* **1956,** 465.
19. Riley, I. H., quoted in ref. 15.

20. Doering, W. von E., and T. C. Ascher, *J. Am. Chem. Soc.*, **75**, 393 (1953).
21. Leonard, N. J., and S. Gelfard, *J. Am. Chem. Soc.*, **77**, 3269 (1955).
22. Barton, D. H. R., *Private communication.*
23. Courtney, J. L., R. M. Gascoigne, and A. Z. Szumer, *J. Chem. Soc.*, **1956**, 2119.
24. Courtney, J. L., R. M. Gascoigne, and A. Z. Szumer, *Chem. & Ind. London*, **1956**, 1479.

CHAPTER 5

THE BIOGENETIC RELATIONSHIPS OF THE TERPENOIDS

The first attempts to propound a biogenetic theory as regards terpenoids were stimulated by the fact that the vast majority of the simpler members of this class of substances had structures which could be built up in principle from two or three "isoprene" units. Although isoprene was obtained by the dry distillation of rubber there was no implication, that isoprene *itself* was the active terpenoid precursor.

With the later elucidation of the structures of more complex terpenoids it was found that this simple rule that terpenoids were theoretically divisible into isoprene units still held good to a very large extent. Recently the entire problem has been reviewed by Ruzicka (1).

The problem of the biosynthesis of the terpenoids can be considered at three successive levels. Firstly, there is the question of the creation of the five-carbon unit. Secondly, there is the manner of combination of these units to give the postulated precursors of the various terpenoid families; and, finally, there is the mechanism of cyclisation and rearrangement of these precursors, or their equivalents, to give the individual terpenoids. It must be stressed that much of this is conjecture and that, in any case, the symbol expressing an intermediate implies also near oxidation-reduction transformation products, etc. Many of the postulated cyclisations have not been performed in the laboratory, and, in fact, it is not certain whether ionic or radical (molecular) processes are involved. On the other hand, the hypothesis, as it at present stands, has been

of use in the elucidation of structures, particularly in the triterpenoid field. Progress is being made in the second and third levels of
biosynthesis, but the nature of the primary processes remains
obscure.

THE FIVE-CARBON FRAGMENT

The five-carbon fragment postulated in the biosynthesis of the
terpenoids probably has its origin in a two-carbon unit. There is
support for this belief in the biosynthesis of labelled cholesterol
from acetic acid labelled both on the methyl and carboxyl carbon
atoms. However, biological systems are a mass of complex equi-
libria, and the precise nature of the process leading to the presumed
five-carbon unit is not known. A likely intermediate suggested was
$\beta : \beta$-dimethylacrylic acid (2) which could arise as shown opposite.
But the substances indicated in this equation were to be qualified
by the saving "or equivalent," the term "equivalent" here expressing an ignorance as to the precise process. Biochemically,
for instance, acetaldehyde and an oxidation stage are "equivalent" to acetic acid. Recently, however, it has been found that
β-hydroxy-β-methyl-δ-valerolactone (I) (the lactone of mevalonic
acid) can be utilised in the biosynthesis of cholesterol and so presumably of lanosterol and squalene; the great extent of the conversion has suggested that the major pathway of cholesterol biosynthesis, at least from (I), is *direct* (as opposed to preliminary cleavage into smaller molecules) (3). Later work indicated that the carboxyl
group of mevalonic acid was probably the carbon atom lost in the
formation of the C_5 unit (4).

The order or manner of linking of such postulated five-carbon
fragments has led to the formulation of the various isoprene "rules."
The most general rule merely expresses the principle that terpenoids should be derivable from these five-carbon units joined in any
manner. A more restricted generalisation, known as the special
isoprene rule, states that the five-carbon units should be joined
head to tail as in (III). However, recent work has suggested that
each particular group of terpenoids has its own special variation of
the more general rule. Finally, another expression states that each

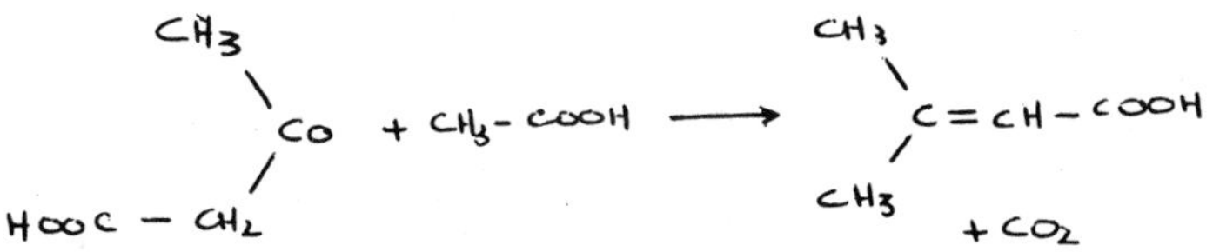

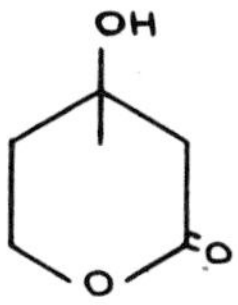

$$CH_3 \quad CO + CH_3-COOH \longrightarrow \quad CH_3 \quad C=CH-COOH$$
$$HOOC-CH_2 \qquad\qquad CH_3 \quad +CO_2$$

(I)

(II)    (III)

of the terpenoid groups should be derivable from hypothetical simple precursors such as squalene, geranylgeraniol, farnesol, etc.
This has been called the biogenetic isoprene rule.

THE MONOTERPENOIDS

Union of two five-carbon units or their equivalent may be presumed to give geraniol (IV). From this the derivation of linaloöl
and the hydrocarbons myrcene and ocimene is obvious. The cyclisation to α-terpineol is known in the laboratory and, in a biochemical system, may result from the ion (V). This is written as a classical carbonium ion, but no restriction as to its detailed identity is
implied. By the transformations shown many of the cyclic monoterpenoids may be derived (1). In these formulae the thick lines
show the five-carbon units. Alternative cyclisations from the hydrocarbons ocimene and myrcene are available.

The compounds derived are all formed, theoretically, from head-
to-tail fusion of C_5 units. A few exceptions are known, for instance,
artemesia ketone and lavandulol.

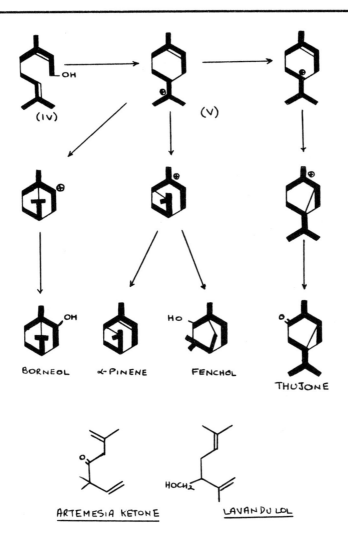

(IV)

(V)

BORNEOL   α-PINENE   FENCHOL

THUJONE

ARTEMESIA KETONE   LAVANDULOL

THE SESQUITERPENOIDS

The key substance in the biogenetic scheme proposed for this group is farnesol (VI). This compound is of particular importance as its dimer difarnesyl (≡ squalene), formed perhaps by the biochemical equivalent of the acyloin condensation, may be a biological precursor of the triterpenoids and steroids. The transformations from farnesol have been postulated to proceed through six-membered and through ten- and eleven-membered ring intermediates. It is interesting that since the promulgation of this theory a ten-membered ring terpenoid, pyrethrosin (VII (or lactonic isomer)), easily cyclised to a substance of the eudesmane type, has been structurally identified (5). The bicyclofarnesol system, also, was not known at that time, but it now seems probable that the lactone iresin (VIII) has this skeleton (6).

Substances which cannot be formed by a farnesol cyclisation are comparatively few. Of these carotol (IX) has one five-carbon unit

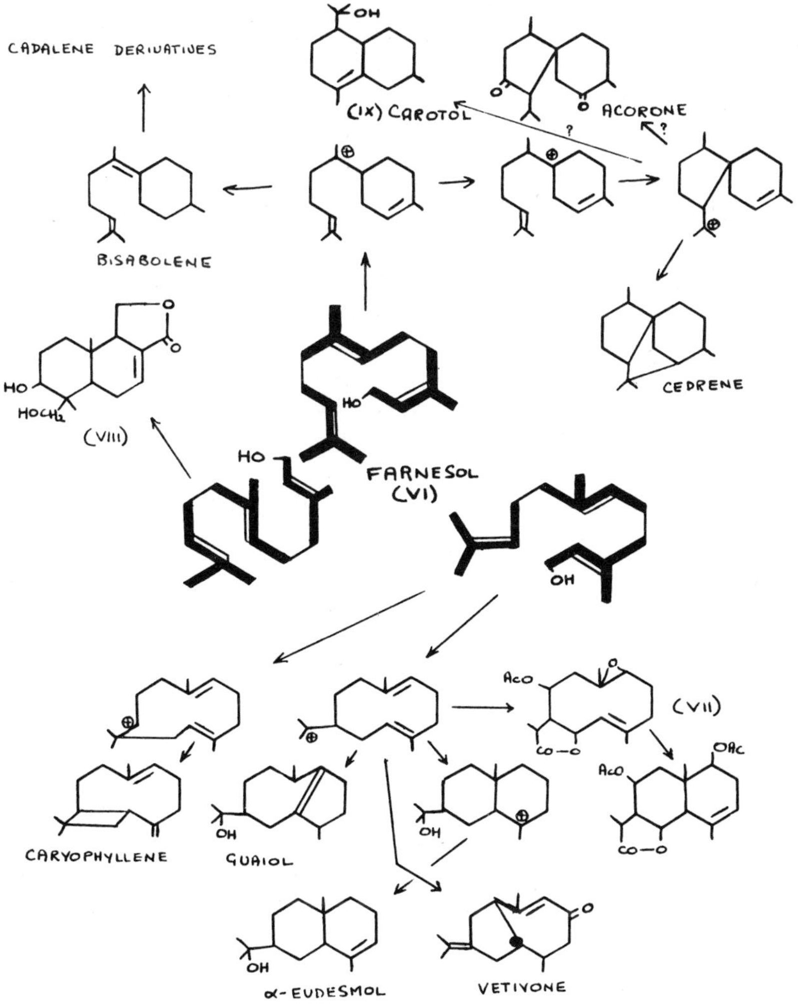
CADALENE DERIVATIVES
(IX) CAROTOL
ACORONE
BISABOLENE
CEDRENE
(VIII)
FARNESOL
(VI)
(VII)
CARYOPHYLLENE
GUAIOL
α-EUDESMOL
VETIVONE

reversed. Zierone (X) also has an isoprenoid, but not *cyclo*farnesol skeleton. On the other hand the ketone eremophilone (XI) is non-isoprenoid. It seems probable that it is formed by rearrangement from a precursor such as (XII).

THE DITERPENOIDS

These substances can be derived, in principle, from geranyl-geraniol (XIII) or related substances. Manool and sclareol are easily obtained, and further transformation leads to the resin acids. Wenkert has suggested (6) that the biogenetic transformation leading to the abietane type acids involves the concerted rearrangement of pimaradienes such as (XIV). He has further suggested that the re-arrangement takes place very readily so that only pimaradienes *epimeric* with (XIV) at C_{13} will be found in nature. This necessitated a revision of the structure of *iso*dextropimaric acid, from (XIV) to (XV). This scheme accommodates also such non-isoprenoid di-

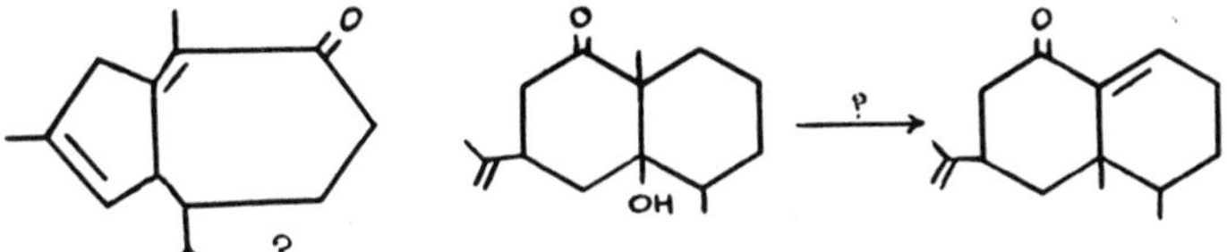

(X)   (XII)   (XI)

(XIII)   CH₂OH   MANOOL

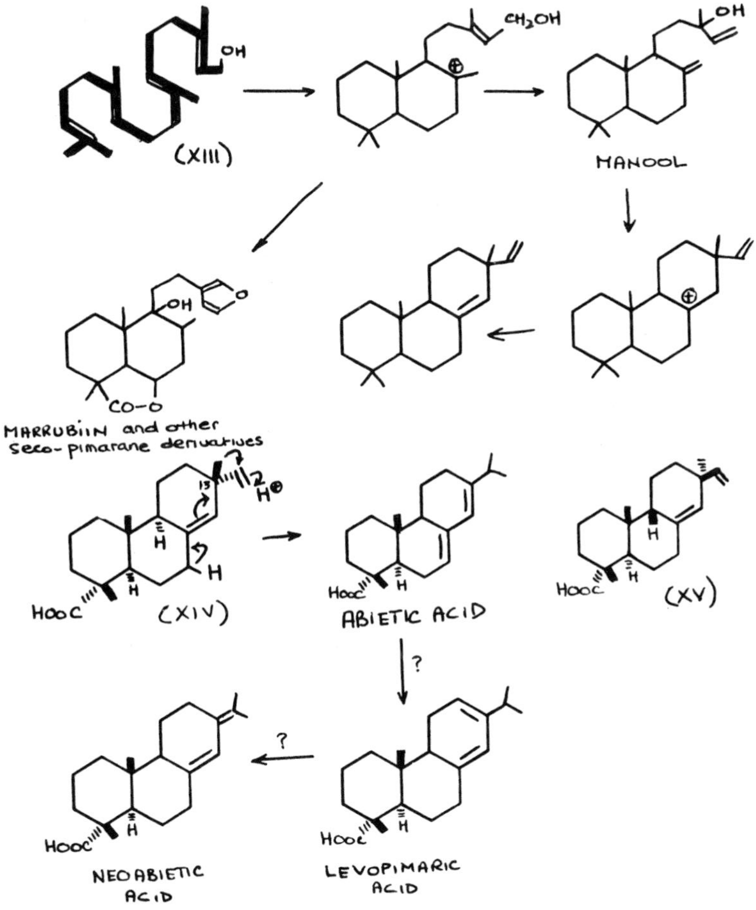

MARRUBIIN and other
Seco-pimarane derivatives

(XIV)   ABIETIC ACID   (XV)

NEOABIETIC
ACID   LEVOPIMARIC
ACID

terpenoids as columbin (XVI) which may perhaps (7) be formed from a *seco*-pimarane derivative (XVII) by the scheme indicated, or its equivalent.

THE TRITERPENOIDS AND STEROIDS

The problem of the biosynthesis of the triterpenoids is intimately associated with that of the steroids. This would be expected, in a sense, in view of the close structural similarity of the tetracyclic triterpenoids, such as lanosterol, to steroids such as cholesterol.

Cholesterol, largely as a result of the brilliant work of Bloch (8), is believed to be formed from a two-carbon fragment. By the use of acetate labelled both on the methyl and carboxyl carbon active cholesterol has been obtained. Bloch also provided evidence that squalene was either in equilibrium with the cholesterol biosynthetic system or else was an intermediate in its formation. Two courses for the cyclisation of squalene were possible, (XVIII) and (XIX), the former being that proposed by Sir Robert Robinson and the latter that proposed by Woodward. The cholesterol derived from such cyclisation will differ in its isotopic distribution at carbon atoms 7, 8, 12, and 13. Degradative work and isolation of relevant carbon atoms has been accomplished by Woodward and Bloch, and by Dauben and by Cornforth and Popjak and their collaborators (9), and strongly supports the Woodward mechanism. Further, stepwise degradation of rings A and B of the steroid nucleus has shown that the similarly labelled carbon atoms are alternately spaced, as predicted by both theories.

Whilst this establishes a relationship between squalene and cholesterol it was not until 1955 (10) that it was shown that lanosterol could be synthesised from acetic acid by rat liver homogenates, and then further converted into cholesterol with loss of three carbon atoms. A subsequent investigation elucidated the remarkable fact that C^{14}-labelled squalene is transformed in different ways depending on the enzyme system. Those systems for the overall synthesis of cholesterol from acetic acid are constituents of the microsomes and of the supernatant fraction of rat liver homogenates. Starting with labelled biosynthesised squalene Bloch and Tchen found that

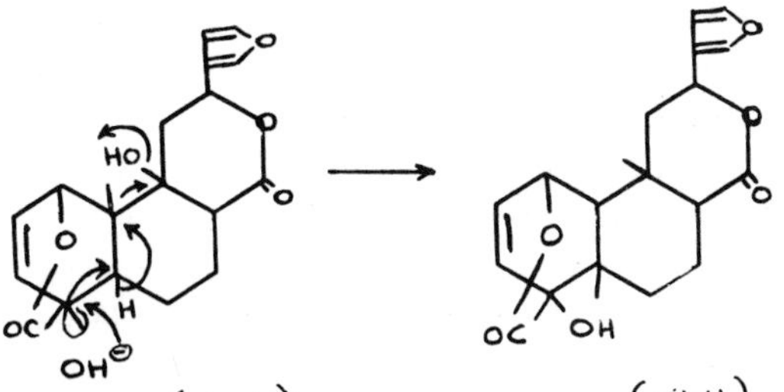

(XVII) (XVI)

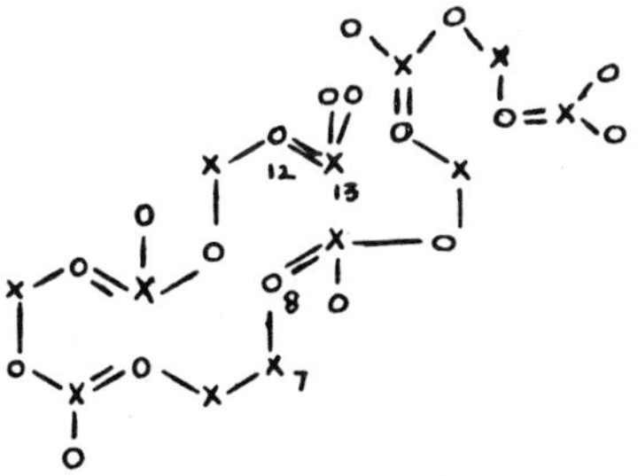

(XVIII)

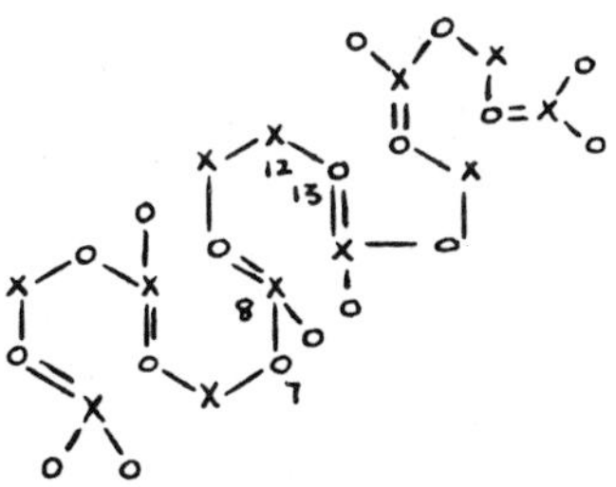

O = ACETATE METHYL
X = ACETATE CARBOXYL

(XIX)

about ten times as much C^{14} is found in cholesterol as in the lanosterol isolated when the enzyme system contained intact microsomes. In the particle-free preparations, however, the C^{14} content of cholesterol is insignificant compared with that of lanosterol. It was therefore concluded that both cyclisation and demethylation may take place with intact microsomes, but although the particle-free preparation may still cyclise it is incapable of demethylating the so-formed lanosterol. This work and other evidence of a related kind have led to the conclusion that the squalene-lanosterol-cholesterol transformation is a major pathway in steroid biogenesis.

The most recent work has been concerned with the biosynthesis of the C_{31} triterpenoid eburicoic acid (XX). The labelled acid was first prepared by allowing *Polyporus sulphureus* to grow in a medium containing *carboxyl*-labelled acetate. Degradation showed that, as in the case of cholesterol, the acetate was utilised as a two-carbon unit, that C_4, C_{11}, and C_{12} were also labelled, and that C_{21} (carboxyl), C_{28}, C_{30}, and C_{31} were *not* labelled (11). By substituting *methyl*-labelled acetate in a similar series of experiments it was found that C_{21}, C_{30}, and C_{31} then became labelled atoms (12). However, the "extra" carbon at C_{28} in the side-chain was still unlabelled, and it was found that it was in fact derived from formate (13).

Stimulated by much of this work, Ruzicka and his colleagues have proposed (14) a comprehensive scheme for the biogenesis of the triterpenoids. Stork and Burgstahler have (15) independently proposed a similar theory. The nature of the ring junction formed by the concerted cyclisation of a triene has already been considered (Volume II), and both groups have stated that a somewhat different path is necessary for the steroids and lanosterol, and for the other triterpenoids. In the processes illustrated opposite and below classical carbonium ions will be used for clarity, but an essential of the transformation scheme is that in the 1 : 2 Wagner-type shifts the stereochemical integrity of the centres involved should be preserved. The first cyclisation scheme leads to euphol and, apparently, tirucallol, though the control of stereochemistry at C_{20} is not entirely clear. After the preliminary proposal (1) of

(XX)

EUPHOL

(XXIII)

TIRUCALLOL

(XXI)

the hypothesis the dammar alcohol (page 114) (XXII) was isolated by Mills. It is clearly derived from the ion (XXI). The intermediate ion (XXIII) then cyclises further to give (XXIV). Rearrangement then leads as shown to the lupeol family. Transformation of (XXIV) may also lead to taraxasterol. Finally, the ion (XXV) is that mentioned in the last chapter (page 182) which may lead by successive shifts to germanicol, β-amyrin, taraxerol, alnusenone (glutinone), and ultimately friedelin. This concerved and stereo-

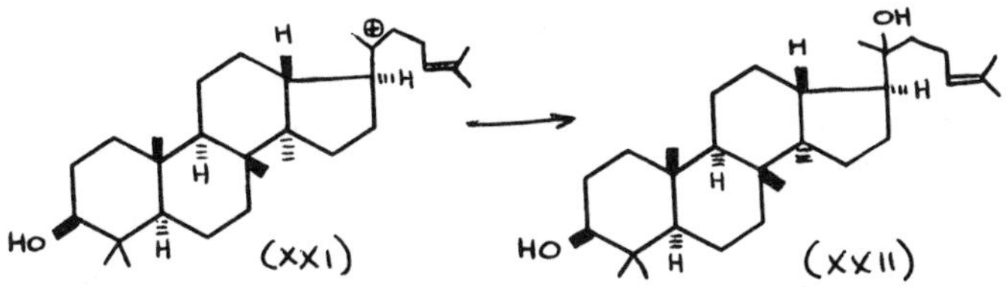

(XXI) → (XXII)

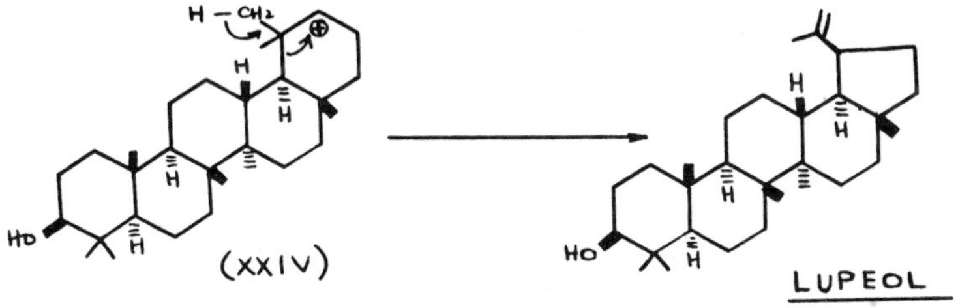

(XXIV) → LUPEOL

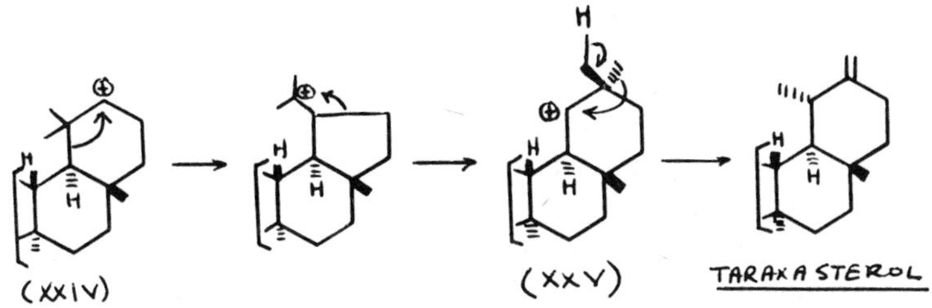

(XXIV) → (XXV) → TARAXASTEROL

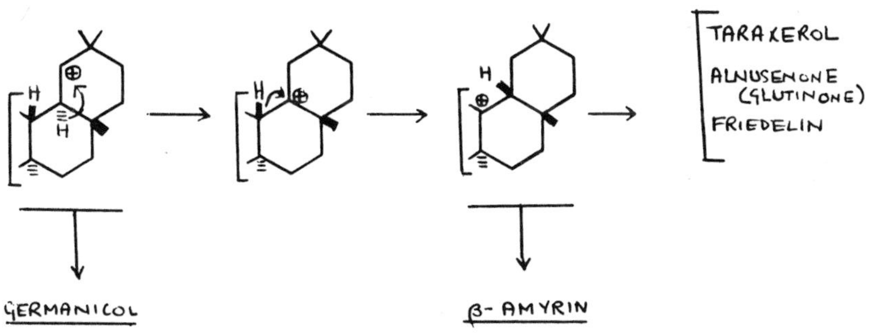

TARAXEROL
ALNUSENONE (GLUTINONE)
FRIEDELIN

GERMANICOL

β-AMYRIN

specific cyclisation of squalene requires that the conformation shown in (XXVI) be adopted prior to cyclisation. Cyclisation from the alternative conformation (XXVII) provides the path to lanosterol and, by demethylation, the steroids.

Onocerin (XXVIII) is clearly a product of cyclisation from both ends of squalene, whilst ambrein (XXIX) is formed by cyclisation from one end as far only as the first ring.

The simplicity and elegence of this hypothesis make it, in essence, very compelling. It is important for its function that these transformations should be concerted, that is, should proceed without the formation of stabilised intermediates. Evidence has very recently been provided, again by Bloch and his associates (16), that the conversion of squalene to lanosterol is, in fact, a concerted process. Squalene, incubated with liver homogenate in the presence of D_2O, was converted into lanosterol with the incorporation of less than 5% of one deuterium atom per molecule. No C——H bonds are formed, therefore, with participation of proton from the solvent. No unsaturated intermediates can be involved, and so the rearrangements postulated must take place by hydride shifts only. Furthermore, the hydroxyl group incorporated into the molecule does not derive from $OH^{\ominus}$ since O^{18} from H_2O^{18} was not incorporated. On the other hand, when squalene was cyclised in an atmosphere of O_2^{18} heavy oxygen *was* introduced into the molecule of lanosterol. The hypothesised "$OH_2^{\oplus}$" must derive, therefore, from oxygen.

(XXVI)

(XXVII)

(XXVIII)

(XXIX)

REFERENCES

1. Ruzicka, L., *Experientia,* 9, 357 (1953).
2. Robinson, R. (Sir), *The Structural Relations of Natural Products,* Clarendon Press, Oxford, 1955, p. 14 *et seq.,* cf. also Bloch, K., L. C. Clarke, and I. Harary, *J. Am. Chem. Soc.,* 76, 3859 (1954).
3. Tavormina, P. A., M. H. Gibbs, and J. W. Huff, *J. Am. Chem. Soc.,* 78, 4499 (1956); Wolf, D. E., C. H. Hoffman, P. E. Aldrich, H. R. Skeggs, L. D. Wright, and K. Folkers, *J. Am. Chem. Soc.,* 78, 4499 (1956).
4. Tavormina, P. A., and M. H. Gibbs, *J. Am. Chem. Soc.,* 78, 210 (1956).
5. Barton, D. H. R., and P. de Mayo, *J. Chem. Soc.,* 1957, 150.
6. Wenkert, E., *Chem. & Ind. (London),* 1955, 282.
7. Barton, D. H. R., and D. Elad, *J. Chem. Soc.,* 1956, 2090.
8. Little, H. N., and K. Bloch, *J. Biol. Chem.,* 183, 33 (1950); Wuersch, J., R. L. Huang, and K. Bloch, *J. Biol. Chem.,* 195, 439 (1952); Bloch, K., L. C. Clarke, and I. Harary, *J. Am. Chem. Soc.,* 76, 3859 (1954).
9. Woodward, R. B., and K. Bloch, *J. Am. Chem. Soc.,* 75, 2023 (1953); Cornforth, J. W., G. D. Hunter, and G. Popjak, *Biochem. J.,* 54, 597 (1953); cf. Popjak, G., *Roy. Inst. Chem. (London) Lectures,* No. 2 (1955); Dauben, W. G., and K. H. Takemura, *J. Am. Chem. Soc.,* 75, 6302 (1953); Dauben, W. G., S. Abraham, S. Hotta, I. L. Chaikoff, H. L. Bradlow, and A. H. Soloway, *J. Am. Chem. Soc.,* 75, 3038 (1953).
10. Clayton, R. B., and K. Bloch, *Federation Proc.,* 14, 194 (1955); Tchen, T. T., and K. Bloch, *J. Am. Chem. Soc.,* 77, 6085 (1955).
11. Dauben, W. G., and J. H. Richards, *J. Am. Chem. Soc.,* 78, 5329 (1956).
12. Dauben, W. G., Y. Ban, and J. H. Richards, *J. Am. Chem. Soc.,* 79, 968 (1957).
13. Dauben, W. G., G. J. Fonken, and G. A. Boswell, *J. Am. Chem. Soc.,* 79, 1000 (1957); see also Danielsson, H., and K. Bloch, *J. Am. Chem. Soc.,* 79, 500 (1957).
14. Eschenmoser, A., L. Ruzicka, O. Jeger, and D. Arigoni, *Helv. Chim. Acta,* 38, 1890 (1955).
15. Stork, G., and A. W. Burgstahler, *J. Am. Chem. Soc.,* 77, 5068 (1955).
16. Tchen, T. T., and K. Bloch, *J. Am. Chem. Soc.,* 78, 1516 (1956).

INDEX

236